BUMPER INSTANT ART

BIBLE WORKSHEETS

BOOK ONE

Kevin Mayhew

First published in 2001 by
KEVIN MAYHEW LTD
Buxhall
Stowmarket
Suffolk IP14 3BW
E-mail: info@kevinmayhewltd.com

9 8 7 6 5 4 3 2 1

ISBN 1 84003 743 1
Catalogue No 1396083

Cover design by Jonathan Stroulger
Typesetting by Elisabeth Bates
Printed and bound in Great Britain

Contents

New Testament

God made it

Draw a little picture for each day of creation See Genesis 1

1	2	3	4	5
6	7			

Help Adam find Eve

Word search

S	E	T	S	E	R	D	I	S	N
T	A	R	T	C	H	N	T	U	F
S	Y	O	C	K	T	A	S	E	R
T	U	K	E	N	R	L	R	W	P
A	H	T	S	E	A	P	E	T	S
R	E	G	N	M	E	M	W	G	K
S	H	S	I	F	O	L	O	S	C
S	T	N	A	L	P	O	L	O	S
F	A	L	O	W	E	R	F	O	N
N	A	P	S	C	E	T	S	D	E

ANIMALS
EARTH
FISH
FLOWERS
INSECTS
LAND
LIGHT
MOON
MAN
PLANTS
REST
SEA
SKY
STARS
SUN

Genesis 3

For as in Adam all die, so in Christ all will be made alive (1 Corinthians 15:22)

Word search

ADAM
CLOTHES
CURSE
DIE
DISOBEYED
EAT
EVE
FRUIT
GARDEN
GROUND
JUDGEMENT
NAKED
PAIN
SNAKE
SWORD
TREE
WEEDS
WOMAN

C	A	M	T	E	S	E	H	T	O	L	C
H	E	S	O	N	V	A	K	E	T	O	K
R	S	D	E	E	W	R	S	N	E	T	E
S	H	M	A	D	A	F	E	N	H	L	D
L	O	T	E	R	O	M	A	N	T	R	E
L	E	S	T	A	E	K	G	R	O	T	U
F	M	I	N	G	E	A	E	W	L	S	W
Y	R	E	D	D	R	O	S	O	C	B	E
E	V	U	R	S	T	O	R	M	I	K	U
T	J	E	I	L	K	A	U	A	A	N	E
B	E	O	Y	T	E	L	C	N	A	K	E
O	D	E	Y	E	B	O	S	I	D	E	L
W	U	I	T	L	F	R	A	A	E	E	R
C	L	O	H	T	E	S	O	P	E	N	S

Cain and Abel

Read this story in Genesis 4

Word search

```
G T N E M H S I N U P O
O C D S C R O P S R O D
P B O E F I N K G L R C
Y R G N A C F N F E C F
I O L C S B L I H J O L
L T I S S H E P R E N O
L H K I L L E L A C I O
N E N E D H R E M R A F
D R T E S O H E P E C S
O J E A L O U S M F R B
P A B E H E B M R A F E
```

ABEL	FIELD	KNIFE
ANGRY	FOOL	PUNISHMENT
BROTHER	GOD	SACRIFICE
CAIN	HATE	SHEEP
CROPS	JEALOUS	SHEPHERD
FARMER	KILL	SIN

We must love one another (1 John 3:11)

Draw a line from Cain to his job and Abel to his job

soldier

potter

brickmaker

stone worker

Cain   Abel

farmer

fisherman

shepherd

How many people are on the boat? ☐

The story of Noah is in Genesis 5, 6, 7, 8 and 9

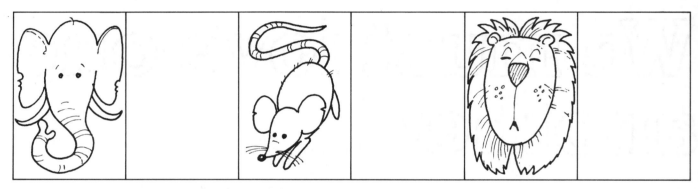

Draw in the other animal in the pair

Word search

ANIMALS	JAPHETH
BOAT	NOAH
DOVE	RAINBOW
FLOOD	RAVEN
HAM	SHEM

J	A	N	I	E	N	O	B
A	W	L	V	M	M	A	H
P	N	O	A	H	J	O	W
H	D	I	B	O	A	T	N
E	O	W	M	N	H	O	E
T	O	O	V	A	I	O	V
H	L	B	M	R	L	A	A
E	F	E	M	E	H	S	R

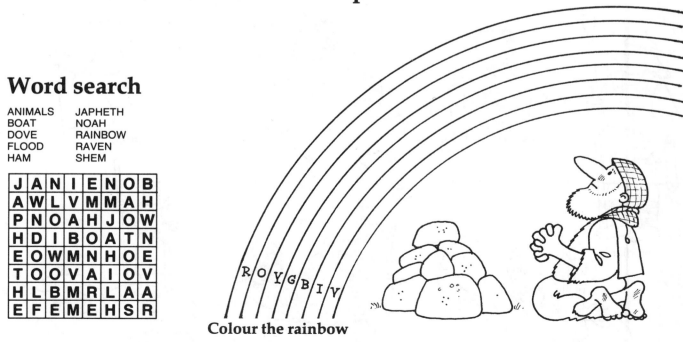

ROYGBIV

Colour the rainbow

Whenever you see a rainbow, remember God is love
— and will never again flood the earth.

Read the story in Genesis 11

Word search

BABEL
BRICKS
CITY
CONFUSE
LANGUAGE
LORD
TAR
TOWER

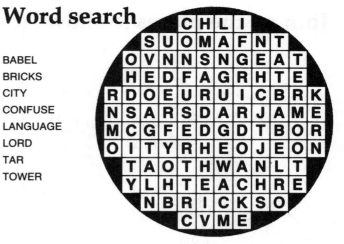

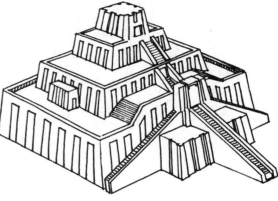

The Tower of Babel may have looked like this.

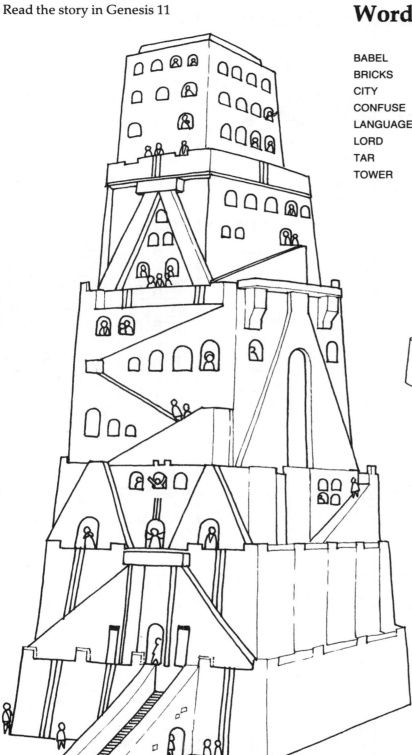

Can you guess these French words and put them in the right places?

tour
s'il vous plaît
merci
aujourd' hui

ENGLISH	FRENCH
please	
thank you	
today	
tower	

God is the Greatest

Join up the places to show Abram's journey from Ur

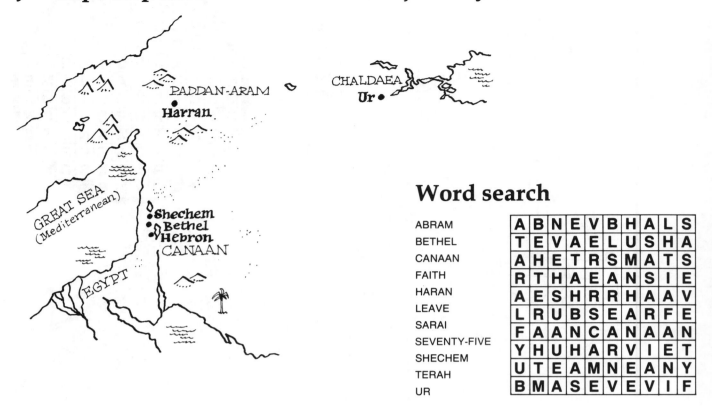

Word search

ABRAM
BETHEL
CANAAN
FAITH
HARAN
LEAVE
SARAI
SEVENTY-FIVE
SHECHEM
TERAH
UR

A	B	N	E	V	B	H	A	L	S
T	E	V	A	E	L	U	S	H	A
A	H	E	T	R	S	M	A	T	S
R	T	H	A	E	A	N	S	I	E
A	E	S	H	R	R	H	A	A	V
L	R	U	B	S	E	A	R	F	E
F	A	A	N	C	A	N	A	A	N
Y	H	U	H	A	R	V	I	E	T
U	T	E	A	M	N	E	A	N	Y
B	M	A	S	E	V	E	V	I	F

By faith Abraham... obeyed and went (Hebrews 11:8)

Abram **75** years old

How many stars can you count here? ☐

Word search

S	A	I	R	I	A	R	A	S	T
C	S	I	A	I	B	M	R	T	I
A	A	T	S	M	A	R	B	A	R
H	O	A	T	H	F	T	A	R	A
I	A	G	A	I	M	H	L	S	H
C	A	R	H	O	F	A	I	T	H
S	B	O	V	A	U	T	E	S	V
A	O	T	A	G	R	I	A	L	S
I	V	I	H	S	T	A	L	H	S
A	A	S	R	O	T	I	S	I	V

ABRAM
ABRAHAM
FAITH
ISAAC
ISHMAEL
LAUGHS
SARAH
SARAI
STARS
VISITORS

Abram **85** years old

Abram tries his own way.

Put on Ishmael's face!

Ishmael (God hears)

Abram **99** years old   Put a tick next to their new names

Abram (Super Dad) ☐   Abraham (Dad of Millions) ☐

Sarai (My princess) ☐   Sarah (Princess of Millions) ☐

Is anything too hard for the Lord? (Genesis 18:14)

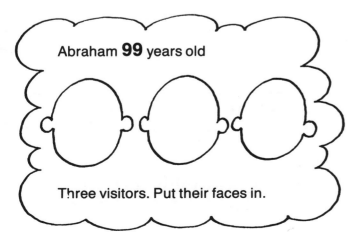

Abraham **99** years old

Three visitors. Put their faces in.

Read the story in Genesis 18 and 19.

Find the way from Sodom to Zoar

40

2   10

How many righteous
people were there in
Sodom?

45

30   3

5   4

1   50   20

100

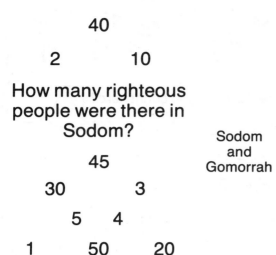

Sodom
and
Gomorrah

Zoar

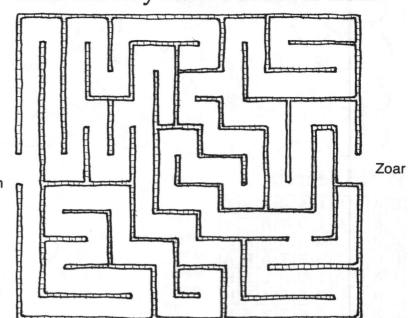

Unjumble these words in the clouds

ROGHORMA

OMODS

TLO

HARAMAB

LATS

Remember Lot's wife

(Luke 17:32)

Genesis 22

Can you see the ram?

Jehovah-Jireh
'God provides'

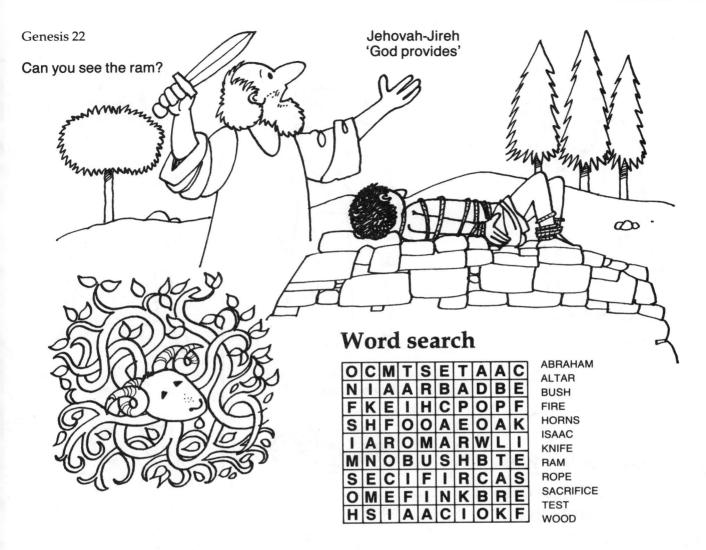

Word search

O	C	M	T	S	E	T	A	A	C
N	I	A	A	R	B	A	D	B	E
F	K	E	I	H	C	P	O	P	F
S	H	F	O	O	A	E	O	A	K
I	A	R	O	M	A	R	W	L	I
M	N	O	B	U	S	H	B	T	E
S	E	C	I	F	I	R	C	A	S
O	M	E	F	I	N	K	B	R	E
H	S	I	A	A	C	I	O	K	F

ABRAHAM
ALTAR
BUSH
FIRE
HORNS
ISAAC
KNIFE
RAM
ROPE
SACRIFICE
TEST
WOOD

To find the name of the place where this happened write the first letter of each picture in each box.

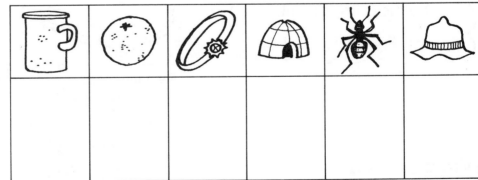

God did not spare his own Son but gave him up for us all (Romans 8:32)

A wife for Isaac

Genesis 24   Servant

Rebecca

Isaac

Qualities in a Wife

Put these qualities
in the order that
you think are
the most important.

☐ A good cook	☐ A good dancer

☐ Generous	☐ Intelligent

☐ Beautiful	☐ A Christian

☐ Wealthy	☐ Fond of children

☐ A good dressmaker	☐ Humorous
	HA HA 

Word search

ABRAHAM	JAR	SERVANT
BETHUEL	LABAN	WATER
CAMELS	PRESENTS	WELL
ISAAC	REBECCA	WIFE

J	Z	P	S	E	R	V	A	N	T
R	A	J	S	L	E	M	A	C	P
E	N	L	L	E	W	A	T	E	R
B	I	C	G	A	F	C	A	D	E
E	C	S	H	G	W	R	B	E	S
C	X	B	A	V	I	S	R	P	E
C	L	A	B	A	N	N	A	D	N
A	O	A	U	J	C	Q	H	E	T
Y	W	I	F	E	G	S	A	C	S
L	E	U	H	T	E	B	M	K	H

Genesis 25 & 27

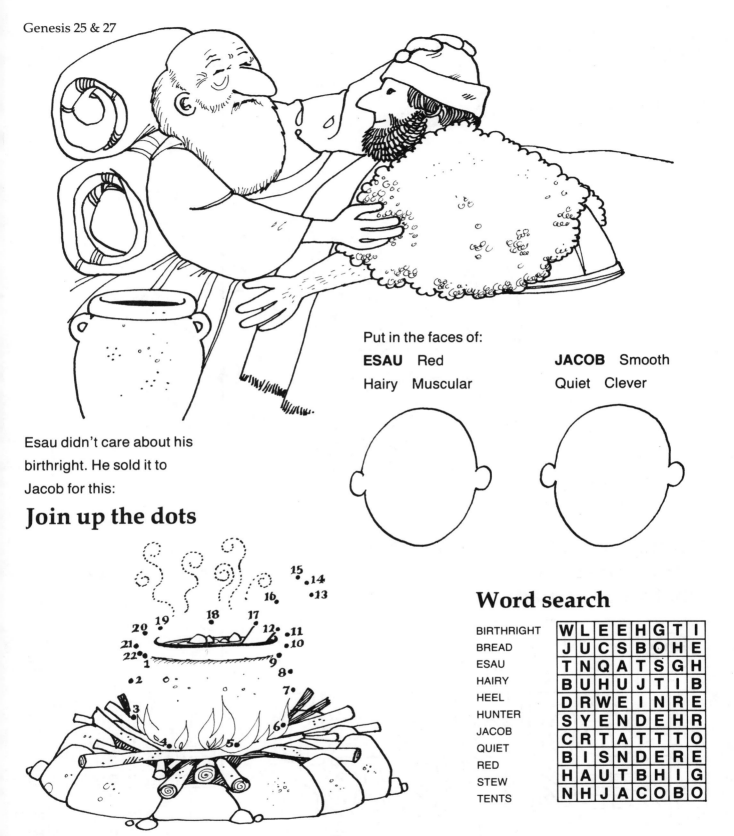

Put in the faces of:

ESAU Red
Hairy Muscular

JACOB Smooth
Quiet Clever

Esau didn't care about his birthright. He sold it to Jacob for this:

Join up the dots

Word search

BIRTHRIGHT
BREAD
ESAU
HAIRY
HEEL
HUNTER
JACOB
QUIET
RED
STEW
TENTS

W	L	E	E	H	G	T	I
J	U	C	S	B	O	H	E
T	N	Q	A	T	S	G	H
B	U	H	U	J	T	I	B
D	R	W	E	I	N	R	E
S	Y	E	N	D	E	H	R
C	R	T	A	T	T	T	O
B	I	S	N	D	E	R	E
H	A	U	T	B	H	I	G
N	H	J	A	C	O	B	O

Do not lie to one another (Colossians 3:9)

We love because he first loved us (1 John 4:19)

Genesis 28

Put the first letter of each picture in the empty box below and find what word is made

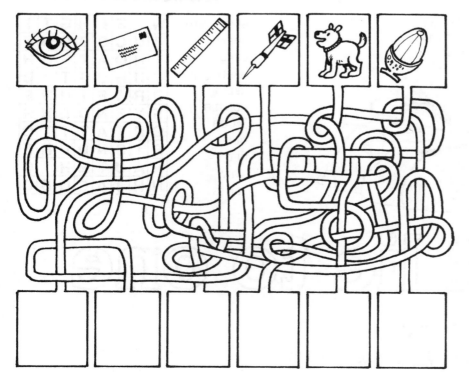

Word search

ANGELS	HEAVEN	PILLAR
BETHEL	JACOB	PILLOW
DREAM	LADDER	STONE
EARTH	OIL	SLEEP

S	E	L	E	B	O	C	A	J	N
R	E	D	D	A	L	G	N	E	L
S	A	O	V	C	E	M	G	B	I
B	R	E	A	N	H	L	E	L	W
R	T	H	O	L	T	N	L	I	O
E	H	T	P	E	E	L	S	V	L
D	S	H	R	V	B	A	G	N	L
D	R	E	A	M	O	V	I	W	I
S	E	E	P	R	A	L	L	I	P
R	H	B	A	C	P	E	A	W	B

Beth el means
House of God

Look up John 1:51
Jesus is the ladder

Read this story in Genesis 32

Jacob said:

I will not let you go unless you bless me

(Genesis 32:26)

Fill in the names of Jacob's sons

| J | A | C | O | B |

Sons of Jacob and Leah

REUBEN
SIMEON
LEVI
JUDAH
ISSACHAR
ZEBULUN

Sons of Jacob and Rachel

JOSEPH
BENJAMIN

Sons of Jacob and Zilpah

GAD
ASHER

Sons of Jacob and Bilhah

DAN
NAPHTALI

You can find the names
in Genesis 35:22-26

You can find this story in Genesis 37

dream 1

dream 2

Love your brothers and sisters

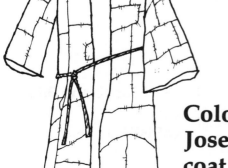

Colour Joseph's coat

Join up these brothers. The first one is done for you.

James	Cain	Peter	Moses	Esau

Aaron	Jacob	John	Andrew	Abel

Word search

BROTHERS
DOTHAN
DREAM
FLOCKS
JOSEPH
ROBE
SHEAVES
SHEEP
STARS
SUN
WELL
WHEAT

D	R	O	T	S	S	B	E	B	E
N	O	S	T	A	N	R	M	R	J
E	W	H	E	A	T	O	A	O	C
B	E	E	K	V	L	L	S	T	F
D	R	E	A	M	A	E	L	H	S
O	O	P	C	K	P	E	L	E	U
T	B	E	O	H	J	P	H	R	W
H	E	E	F	L	O	C	K	S	B
A	S	L	P	E	S	E	P	H	E
N	U	S	H	O	C	K	S	E	T

Joseph and Potiphar's wife

Read the story in Genesis 39

Temptation

Break the code to read the message!

3	10	9	11		5	7	12	4		11	6	4

3	4	12	7	8		1		2	6	1	9	2	4

Ephesians 4:27

a	c	d	e	g	h	i	l	n	o	t	v
1	2	3	4	5	6	7	8	9	10	11	12

Say NO to temptation

Word search

HOUSE   POTIPHAR   SCREAMED
JOSEPH   PRISON   SERVANT
KING   ROBE   SIN

S	T	R	V	A	N	G	T
C	N	S	C	R	N	J	N
R	A	H	P	I	T	O	P
E	V	A	K	V	S	S	H
A	R	I	N	I	S	E	S
M	E	N	R	U	N	P	E
E	S	P	S	O	J	H	J
D	T	E	H	S	B	R	O
E	B	H	O	U	S	E	R

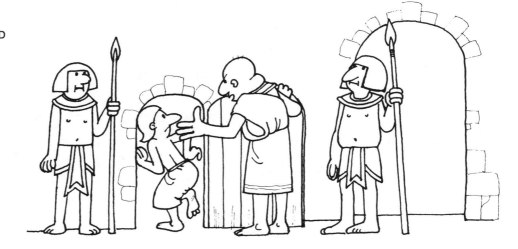

Read the story in Genesis 40 and 41

Chief Baker's Dream

Joseph

Wine Steward's Dream

Pharaoh's Dream

Can you fit these words in?

3 LETTERS
FAT

4 LETTERS
CORN
COWS
THIN

5 LETTERS
BAKER
DREAM
EGYPT
SEVEN
YEARS

6 LETTERS
FAMINE
JOSEPH
PLENTY

7 Years of Plenty

7 Years of Famine

Joseph's family reunited

Find the story in Genesis 42-46

Forgive others

(Luke 6:37)

Write down the names of the people in your family:-

Word search

N	I	M	A	J	N	E	B	S	R	A	E	Y	U	B
E	E	G	Y	P	T	M	A	E	R	D	C	L	O	R
R	S	V	A	C	O	N	O	S	E	Y	G	R	I	O
D	R	I	E	N	R	T	Y	S	E	O	T	M	P	N
L	I	V	E	S	T	O	C	K	D	I	N	I	U	R
I	F	Y	A	S	H	E	P	R	O	R	P	S	C	E
H	D	C	F	V	N	E	H	S	O	G	R	S	N	V
C	K	R	E	D	E	V	P	C	F	E	S	I	A	O
J	U	D	A	H	O	I	E	H	H	O	M	N	A	G
S	C	N	O	N	E	L	S	T	E	A	D	G	N	N
O	T	U	H	S	K	C	O	L	F	R	E	A	A	I
S	F	A	T	H	E	R	J	G	O	O	D	B	C	K
O	J	A	C	O	B	Y	O	U	N	G	E	S	T	E

BAG	EGYPT	KING
BENJAMIN	EVIL	LIVESTOCK
BROTHERS	FAMINE	MISSING
BUY	FATHER	MONEY
CANAAN	FLOCKS	NILE
CHILDREN	FOOD	SACK
CITY	GOD	SEVEN
CORN	GOOD	SHEPHERDS
CROPS	GOSHEN	SON
CUP	GOVERNOR	SPIES
DESCENDANTS	JACOB	YEARS
DRANK	JOSEPH	YOUNGEST
DREAM	JUDAH	

Find this story in Exodus 1 and 2

See if you can de-code this:

Exodus 2:10

Some Egyptian Writing

Find this story in Exodus 3

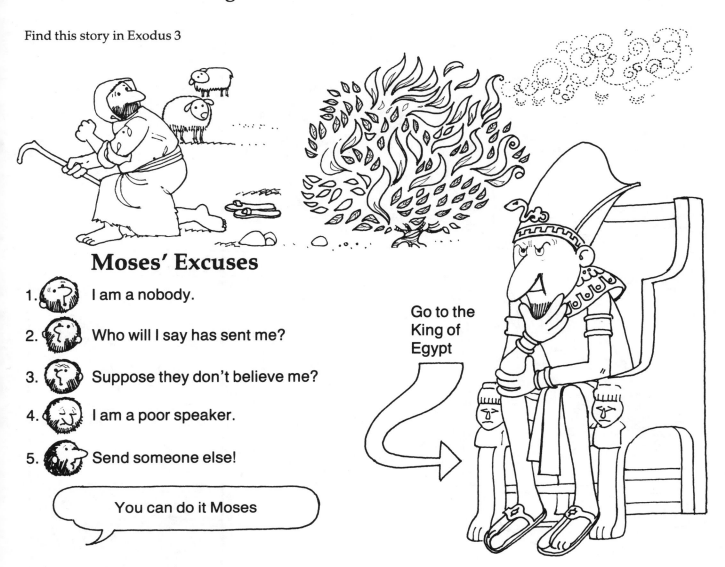

Moses' Excuses

1. I am a nobody.

2. Who will I say has sent me?

3. Suppose they don't believe me?

4. I am a poor speaker.

5. Send someone else!

You can do it Moses

Go to the King of Egypt

I will be with you

(Exodus 3:12)

Lead Moses to the burning bush

Word search

AFRAID   EGYPT   RESCUE
BURNING   GROUND   SANDALS
BUSH   HOLY   SHEEP
DESERT   MOSES

B	U	P	P	E	E	H	S	E	R	T
U	E	R	E	S	C	U	A	G	H	E
H	T	E	G	R	O	U	N	D	E	R
E	P	Y	M	E	E	I	D	P	R	T
D	G	R	O	O	N	E	A	E	S	P
E	I	B	C	R	S	C	L	P	E	Y
S	S	A	U	E	A	E	S	H	E	G
C	O	B	R	S	R	E	S	C	U	E
U	M	T	M	F	H	O	L	Y	P	Y
E	G	Y	P	S	A	F	M	S	A	S

1 BLOOD

2 FROGS

3 GNATS

4 FLIES

5 DEATH OF ANIMALS

6 BOILS

7 HAIL

8 LOCUSTS

9 DARKNESS

10 DEATH OF FIRSTBORN

Find Moses and Aaron's stick in each picture — except one!

This story is in Exodus chapters 7 to 12

Word search

ANIMALS	DEATH	GNATS
BLOOD	FIRSTBORN	HAIL
BOILS	FLIES	LOCUSTS
DARKNESS	FROGS	MOSES

N	R	O	B	T	S	R	I	F	D
D	S	O	O	L	B	A	B	M	A
M	G	S	T	A	N	G	O	F	R
U	O	H	A	I	L	S	I	R	K
C	R	S	M	S	E	I	L	F	N
S	F	A	E	S	B	O	S	C	E
B	L	O	O	D	E	A	T	H	S
S	T	S	U	C	O	L	F	O	S

Word search

```
B R E I A D A E R B W O O L E
A R O N R O B T S R I F E W N
O M E S D O R L I H N T S E R
S I F T E L U P O R E S T B R
E D O R C B M A L O S R C E E
I N E S L O U S T A E H B O R
R I J T A D I S S O G M H S S
O G F F S Y B O O L E U T T R
G H U C T A O V E M P H E W I
T T U F S S O E E V H H E R T
G P H J U R E R F Y A Y O O P
S E Y S P I I A W O R S C U Y
R U E G P F A S D O A S T E D
O J E S E M A R F R O O D E S
P L O I R S C V E R H P O N S
```

BITTER	FIRE	MIDNIGHT
BLOOD	FIRSTBORN	PASSOVER
BODY	HERBS	PHARAOH
BREAD	HYSSOP	PLAGUE
CUP	JESUS	REMEMBER
DOORFRAME	LAMB	ROASTED
EGYPT	LAST SUPPER	WINE

The story is in Exodus 11 and 12

Break the code to read the message!

Y___ m_s_ r_m_v_ _h_ ___d
 2 5   5 4   3 2 3   4 3   2 6

y__as__ __f sin s_ __ha_ y___ wi___ b_
 3 4 2   2 4   4   2 5   6 6   3

__n_ir___y p_r_.
 3 4 3 6   5 6 3

o = 2, e = 3, t = 4,
u = 5, l = 6

Christ, our Passover Lamb has been sacrificed
(1 Corinthians 5:7)

Word search

E	P	I	L	L	A	R	A	W
S	G	S	E	S	R	O	H	A
T	L	Y	R	D	E	A	S	T
O	C	M	P	E	G	S	H	E
I	L	R	Y	T	N	T	O	R
R	O	A	M	A	I	R	I	M
A	U	G	N	A	K	A	E	O
H	D	Y	F	D	W	I	N	D
C	H	D	N	A	H	A	E	S

ARMY   FAITH   MOSES
CHARIOTS   HAND   PILLAR
CLOUD   HORSES   RED
DRY   KING   SEA
EAST   LAND   WATER
EGYPTIANS   MIRIAM   WIND

Find this story
in Exodus
14 and 15

By faith the people passed through the Red Sea (Hebrews 11:29)

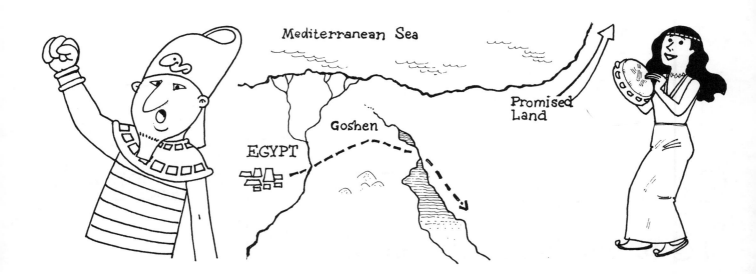

The Ten Commandments are listed in
Exodus 20:1-17 and Deuteronomy 5:1-21

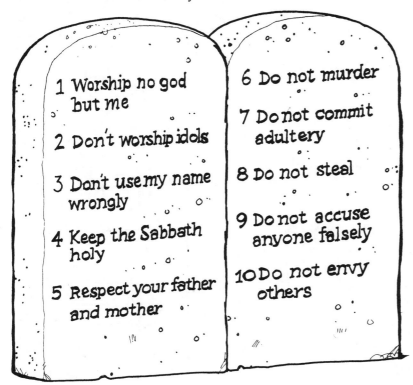

1 Worship no god but me

2 Don't worship idols

3 Don't use my name wrongly

4 Keep the Sabbath holy

5 Respect your father and mother

6 Do not murder

7 Do not commit adultery

8 Do not steal

9 Do not accuse anyone falsely

10 Do not envy others

Which instruction manual belongs to which item?

I will put my laws in their hearts

(Hebrews 10:16)

Jesus explained these laws in Matthew 5:17-48

1 These can become our 'gods'

2 Be careful about making idols

3 Watch your language

4 I haven't got time for worship

5 Respect your Parents

6 I HATE YOU! — Hateful words are like murder

7 Gor! I want her — Be careful about your thoughts

8 SWEET SHOP — Don't steal

9 SHE TOOK MY PENCIL — Be careful who you accuse

10 I want that bike — Don't covet

Read the story in Exodus 32

**Which way up the
mountain?**

Don't make idols

(Exodus 20:4)

**What you spend your time and money
on can become an idol.**

Are any of these your idols?

Word search

A	E	M	O	S	E	S	G	O	I
A	N	I	D	L	A	T	L	D	G
R	M	G	O	A	R	O	O	N	S
N	G	R	R	E	R	N	I	O	T
O	E	O	G	Y	I	C	R	Y	O
B	N	M	O	U	N	T	A	I	N
A	U	E	L	A	G	O	L	D	E
D	G	L	D	E	S	T	R	O	Y
N	B	I	L	T	A	I	N	L	S
E	C	I	F	I	R	C	A	S	Y

AARON DESTROY MOSES
ANGRY EARRINGS MOUNTAIN
BULL GOLD SACRIFICE
DANCING IDOLS STONE

Moses and the spies

Read this story in Numbers 13

How many happy spies can you see? ☐

**Put a ring around those things which you think
the spies might have taken with them**

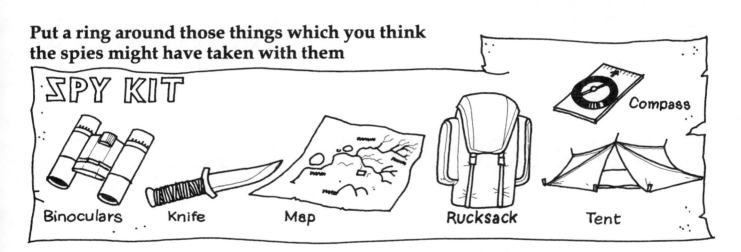

SPY KIT

Binoculars Knife Map Rucksack Tent Compass

Different kinds of fruit

3 LETTERS

FIG

4 LETTERS

DATE
PEAR
PLUM

5 LETTERS

APPLE
GRAPE
LEMON
MANGO
MELON
PEACH

6 LETTERS

BANANA
CHERRY
ORANGE

7 LETTERS

AVOCADO

10 LETTERS

STRAWBERRY

11 LETTERS

POMEGRANATE

Read this story in Joshua 6

...and the walls collapsed

(Joshua 6:20)

Word search

T	R	U	M	P	E	T	S	E	P
I	N	J	O	S	H	U	A	T	R
C	O	A	E	M	A	R	C	H	I
Y	W	T	N	R	N	E	A	X	E
I	A	S	R	E	I	D	L	O	S
G	L	R	V	O	V	C	X	B	T
A	L	E	M	T	U	O	H	S	S
O	S	G	D	Y	T	I	C	O	B

ARMY
BOX
CITY
COVENANT
GATES
JERICHO
JOSHUA
MARCH

PRIESTS
SEVEN
SHOUT
SOLDIERS
TRUMPETS
WALLS

Rescue route

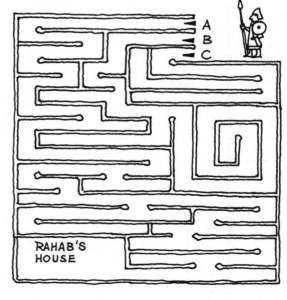

RAHAB'S HOUSE

Which is the rescue route to Rahab's House?

Read the story in Joshua 7

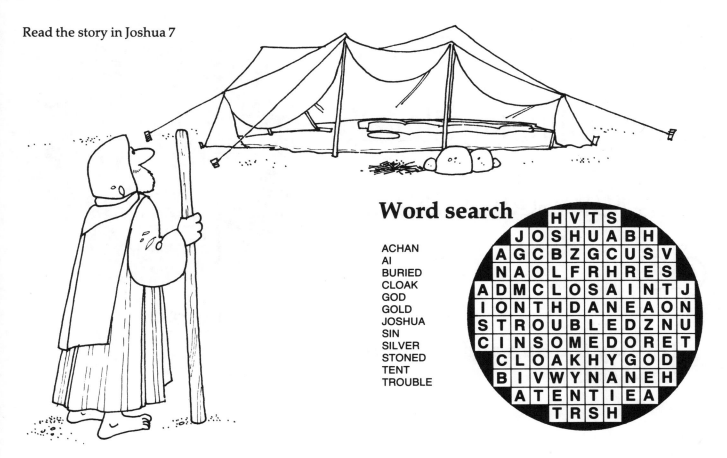

Word search

ACHAN
AI
BURIED
CLOAK
GOD
GOLD
JOSHUA
SIN
SILVER
STONED
TENT
TROUBLE

```
        H V T S
   J O S H U A B H
 A G C B Z G C U S V
 N A O L F R H R E S
A D M C L O S A I N T J
 I O N T H D A N E A O N
 S T R O U B L E D Z N U T
 C I N S O M E D O R E T
 C L O A K H Y G O D
 B I V W Y N A N E H
 A T E N T I E A
        T R S H
```

EH SWONK EHT STERCES FO EHT TRAEH

The words are written backwards — unjumble them

Psalm 44:21

Here are other ways of being dishonest:-

Keeping things you find

Pretending

Cheating in a test

Playing games unfairly

Keeping the change

Taking sweets without asking

Bringing home school pencils

① ② ③

Find the way to Achan's tent

For there is nothing that God cannot do

(Luke 1:37)

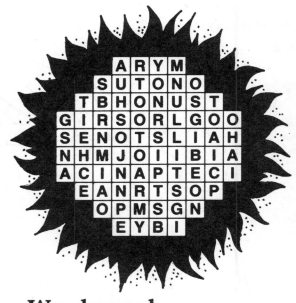

Word search

ARMY	JOSHUA	STILL
GIBEON	MOON	SUN
HAILSTONES	PANIC	TROOPS

The day the Sun and the Moon stood still

Find this story in Joshua 10

Colour these powerful things, but remember: Our God is more powerful than any of these

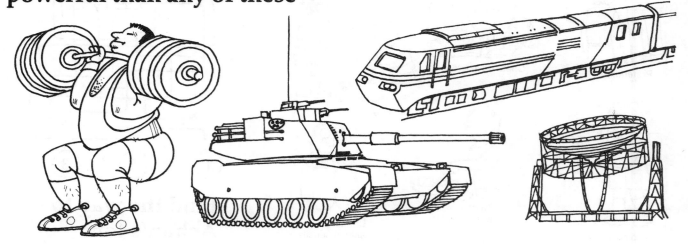

Judges 13 and 14

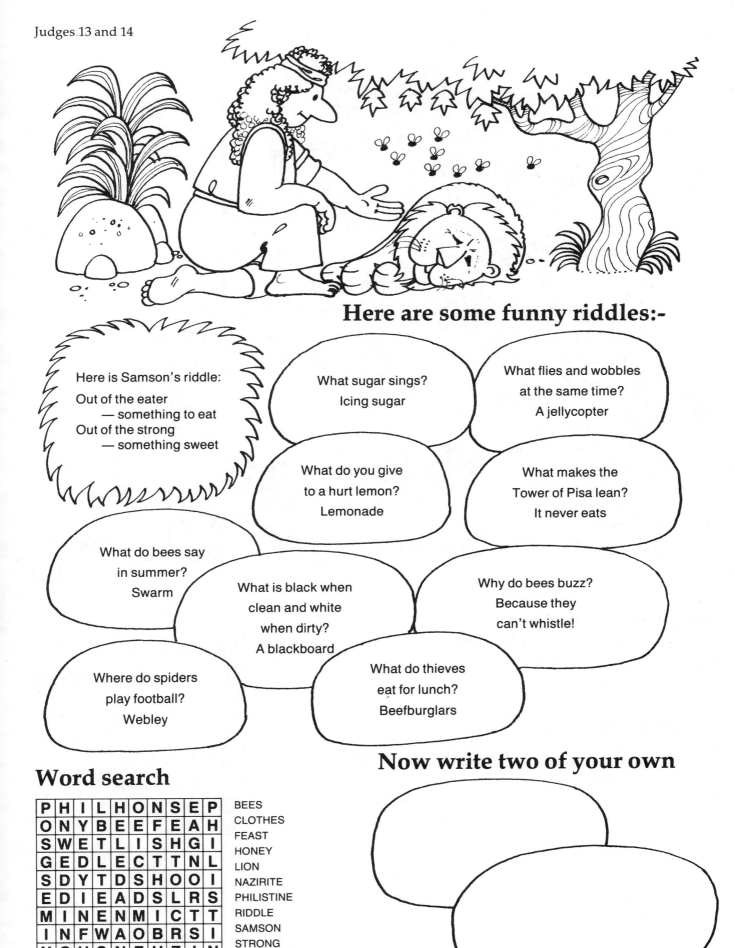

Here are some funny riddles:-

Here is Samson's riddle:

Out of the eater
— something to eat
Out of the strong
— something sweet

What sugar sings?
Icing sugar

What flies and wobbles
at the same time?
A jellycopter

What do you give
to a hurt lemon?
Lemonade

What makes the
Tower of Pisa lean?
It never eats

What do bees say
in summer?
Swarm

What is black when
clean and white
when dirty?
A blackboard

Why do bees buzz?
Because they
can't whistle!

Where do spiders
play football?
Webley

What do thieves
eat for lunch?
Beefburglars

Now write two of your own

Word search

P	H	I	L	H	O	N	S	E	P
O	N	Y	B	E	E	F	E	A	H
S	W	E	T	L	I	S	H	G	I
G	E	D	L	E	C	T	T	N	L
S	D	Y	T	D	S	H	O	O	I
E	D	I	E	A	D	S	L	R	S
M	I	N	E	N	M	I	C	T	T
I	N	F	W	A	O	B	R	S	I
Y	G	H	S	N	E	H	Z	I	N
R	E	T	I	R	I	Z	A	N	E

BEES
CLOTHES
FEAST
HONEY
LION
NAZIRITE
PHILISTINE
RIDDLE
SAMSON
STRONG
SWEET
WEDDING

The Battle of Jawbone Hill

Read the story in Judges 15.

With a donkey's jawbone
  I have made donkeys of them
With a donkey's jawbone
  I have killed a thousand men.

Which stories are these?

A small lunch (Luke 9)	A small stone (1 Samuel 17)
A small girl (2 Kings 5)	A small coin (Luke 15)
7 times	

Word search

E	K	N	O	D	O	N	E	Y	P	S	T
L	L	I	K	C	O	R	E	T	A	M	O
X	O	F	E	S	F	N	S	H	I	A	Y
D	A	T	M	C	O	S	K	O	R	L	R
E	M	A	T	B	X	E	L	E	S	L	O
L	S	C	W	Y	E	H	S	I	Y	I	T
L	T	A	I	L	S	C	O	R	N	K	C
I	J	V	P	R	A	R	I	S	Y	E	I
K	E	E	O	L	V	O	C	D	R	O	V
P	H	I	L	I	S	T	I	N	E	S	E
V	I	T	C	D	N	A	S	U	O	H	T

CAVE	KILLED	TAILS
CORN	PAIRS	THOUSAND
DONKEY	PHILISTINES	TORCHES
ETAM	ROCK	VICTORY
FOXES	SAMSON	
JAWBONE	SMALL	

Samson and Delilah

Read the story in Judges 16

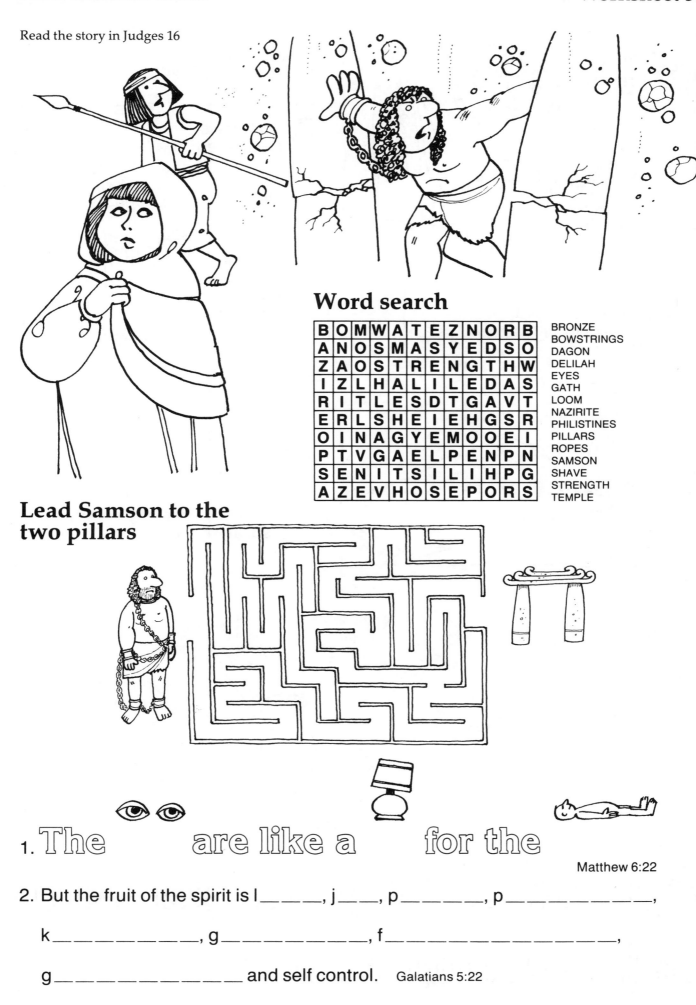

Word search

B	O	M	W	A	T	E	Z	N	O	R	B
A	N	O	S	M	A	S	Y	E	D	S	O
Z	A	O	S	T	R	E	N	G	T	H	W
I	Z	L	H	A	L	I	L	E	D	A	S
R	I	T	L	E	S	D	T	G	A	V	T
E	R	L	S	H	E	I	E	H	G	S	R
O	I	N	A	G	Y	E	M	O	O	E	I
P	T	V	G	A	E	L	P	E	N	P	N
S	E	N	I	T	S	I	L	I	H	P	G
A	Z	E	V	H	O	S	E	P	O	R	S

BRONZE
BOWSTRINGS
DAGON
DELILAH
EYES
GATH
LOOM
NAZIRITE
PHILISTINES
PILLARS
ROPES
SAMSON
SHAVE
STRENGTH
TEMPLE

Lead Samson to the two pillars

1. The 👁👁 are like a 🪔 for the 🛏

Matthew 6:22

2. But the fruit of the spirit is l _ _ _ _, j _ _ _, p _ _ _ _ _, p _ _ _ _ _ _ _ _,

k _ _ _ _ _ _ _ _ _, g _ _ _ _ _ _ _ _, f _ _ _ _ _ _ _ _ _ _ _,

g _ _ _ _ _ _ _ _ _ _ _ and self control.   Galatians 5:22

1 Hannah's Prayer

Find these stories in 1 Samuel chapters 1, 2 and 3

2 Samuel is Dedicated

3 The Lord speaks to Samuel

Put a ring around the ways in which God can speak to us

In dreams

Using other people

By Phone

By Post

From the Bible

Our conscience

Speak Lord, your servant is listening (1 Samuel 3:9)

Man looks at the outward appearance but the Lord looks at the heart

(1 Samuel 16:7)

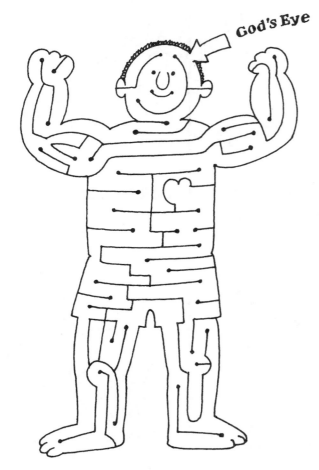

God's Eye

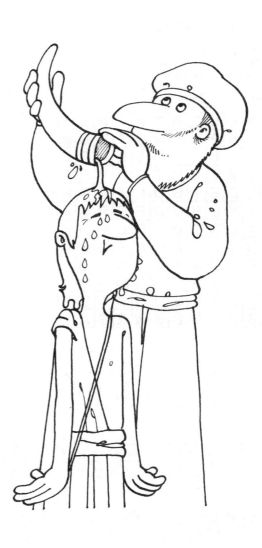

Word search

T	H	E	S	E	W	O	R	D	S	E	A	R	C
I	T	S	T	E	G	E	R	A	B	H	S	E	H
N	G	A	D	K	H	A	H	E	A	R	T	A	D
E	D	M	V	I	E	B	T	M	I	R	P	E	O
E	J	U	B	N	V	H	M	T	L	P	S	L	H
S	H	E	P	G	L	A	O	I	E	L	I	S	O
O	P	L	S	E	H	E	D	A	I	V	E	R	H
P	E	E	H	S	M	B	R	I	E	E	F	J	E
S	T	E	A	L	E	A	L	O	I	K	E	S	S
E	M	R	G	A	N	O	I	N	T	N	G	H	I
D	R	A	H	C	G	L	N	I	T	T	E	G	E
H	E	S	E	C	I	F	I	R	C	A	S	A	R
C	R	A	E	S	D	R	O	W	E	S	E	H	T

ANOINT
APPEARANCE
BETHLEHEM
DAVID
ELIAB
HEART
JESSE
KING
OLIVE OIL
SACRIFICE
SAMUEL
SHAMMAH
SHEEP

The story is in 1 Samuel 17

Word search

ARMOUR   FIVE   SHIELD
BATTLE   GOLIATH   SPEAR
CATAPULT   JAVELIN   STONES
DAVID   PHILISTINE   SWORD
DEAD   SAUL

H	T	L	U	P	A	T	A	C	H	E	T
O	H	E	P	H	I	N	S	T	U	B	M
L	G	O	L	I	I	S	L	L	A	D	O
G	I	V	E	L	H	T	J	U	V	R	R
O	L	D	E	I	G	O	L	I	A	T	H
F	I	V	E	S	D	N	E	E	R	S	A
D	A	L	W	T	D	E	P	B	M	D	E
J	D	O	L	I	F	S	A	F	O	E	H
O	R	U	V	N	E	T	E	D	U	O	R
D	V	A	I	E	T	H	R	M	R	M	R
H	D	S	I	L	E	D	U	S	A	L	E
W	S	O	E	D	R	S	W	E	B	A	L

Circle ten differences in these two pictures

The one who is in you is greater than the one who is in the world (1 John 4:4)

Look up this story in the Bible 2 Samuel 6:12-23

Word search

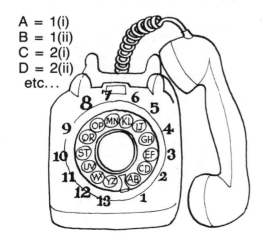

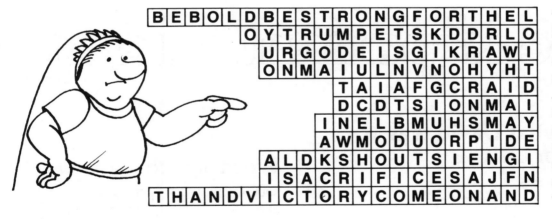

B	E	B	O	L	D	B	E	S	T	R	O	N	G	F	O	R	T	H	E	L
	O	Y	T	R	U	M	P	E	T	S	K	D	D	R	L	O				
	U	R	G	O	D	E	I	S	G	I	K	R	A	W	I					
	O	N	M	A	I	U	L	N	V	N	O	H	Y	H	T					
		T	A	I	A	F	G	C	R	A	I	D								
		D	C	D	T	S	I	O	N	M	A	I								
		I	N	E	L	B	M	U	H	S	M	A	Y							
		A	W	M	O	D	U	O	R	P	I	D	E							
	A	L	D	K	S	H	O	U	T	S	I	E	N	G	I					
	I	S	A	C	R	I	F	I	C	E	S	A	J	F	N					
T	H	A	N	D	V	I	C	T	O	R	Y	C	O	M	E	O	N	A	N	D

ARK
DANCING
DAVID
FOOL
HUMBLE
JERUSALEM
KING
MICHAL
PROUD
SACRIFICES
SHOUTS
TRUMPETS

Here's how to break the code

A = 1(i)
B = 1(ii)
C = 2(i)
D = 2(ii)
etc...

4(i) 8(i) 2(ii) 8(i) 8(ii) 8(ii) 8(i) 10(i) 3(i) 10(i) 10(ii) 4(ii) 3(i)

— — — | — — — — — — — — | — — —

8(ii) 9(ii) 8(i) 11(i) 2(ii) 1(ii) 11(i) 10(ii) 4(i) 5(i) 11(ii) 3(i) 10(i)

— — — — — | — — — | — — — — —

4(i) 9(ii) 1(i) 2(i) 3(i) 10(ii) 8(i) 10(ii) 4(ii) 3(i)

— — — — — | — — | — — —

4(ii) 11(i) 7(i) 1(ii) 6(ii) 3(i)

— — — — — —   James 4:6

Can you find the way to and from the well from the cave?

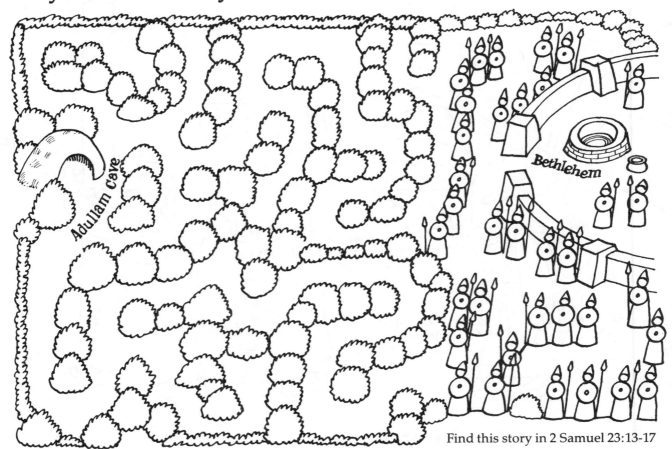

Find this story in 2 Samuel 23:13-17

Love is patient and kind

(1 Corinthians 13:4)

Draw in what David was longing for 2 Samuel 23:15

Word search

ADULLAM
BETHLEHEM
DAVID
DRINK
GATE
HARVEST
LOVE
PHILISTINES
POURED
SOLDIERS
WATER
WELL
UNSELFISH

B	E	T	H	A	M	P	T	O	P	N	E
A	U	C	E	L	D	A	D	V	H	D	A
K	N	D	I	N	B	G	I	T	I	E	F
E	S	E	F	I	E	S	V	M	L	H	I
S	E	R	V	L	T	O	A	L	I	D	S
H	L	U	A	O	H	L	D	R	S	V	E
S	F	O	I	D	L	E	B	R	T	S	T
L	I	P	E	U	E	H	E	M	I	A	D
L	S	I	D	P	H	E	H	S	N	N	H
U	H	A	R	V	E	S	T	W	E	T	K
A	O	V	E	L	M	E	L	A	S	B	E
D	P	O	U	T	E	D	E	T	G	S	F
U	S	O	M	E	F	L	L	E	W	H	I
M	L	S	O	L	D	I	E	R	S	T	H
O	V	E	S	H	D	E	N	O	P	S	P
K	I	N	G	A	T	S	E	F	V	O	H

Read the story in
1 Kings 3:16-28

Trust in the Lord with all your heart and lean not on your own understanding

(Proverbs 3:5)

Can you help the lady find her baby?

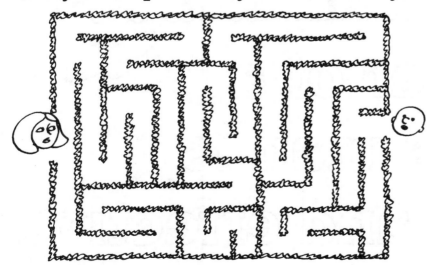

Can you find 12 hidden words about the story?

1._____ 2._____

3._____ 4._____

5._____ 6._____

7._____

8._____

9._____

10._____

11._____

12._____

A	B	E	S	W	L	I
M	O	C	H	I	L	D
G	U	K	V	S	W	G
T	N	I	K	D	Y	D
H	N	I	I	O	B	R
G	H	E	N	M	A	O
I	D	O	G	R	B	W
N	O	M	O	L	O	S
P	E	E	L	S	A	M

Read the story in 1 Kings 17

Word search

AHAB   DEW   RAIN
BREAD   ELIJAH   RAVENS
BROOK   MEAT   WATER
CHERITH PRAYER

D	R	E	W	N	S	W	A	E	H
L	I	J	S	H	R	C	W	A	T
B	E	D	N	A	S	E	C	H	I
S	A	J	E	J	D	H	T	H	R
E	T	H	V	I	M	I	P	A	Y
H	D	I	A	L	R	Y	T	E	W
V	A	E	R	E	Y	A	R	P	A
R	E	A	H	S	E	W	I	H	S
S	R	C	S	M	V	A	R	N	M
C	B	R	O	O	K	W	A	T	E

The prayer of a righteous man is powerful and effective

(James 5:16)

1 Kings 17

Give and it will be given to you. A good measure pressed down, shaken together and running over will be poured into your lap (Luke 6:38)

Word search

O	Z	A	P	N	G	L	O	R
H	S	W	O	D	I	W	G	O
E	T	H	E	A	D	I	N	R
I	N	A	S	J	Z	L	I	O
S	T	J	H	K	C	I	R	N
H	F	I	E	P	C	K	E	J
Z	A	L	M	O	E	I	H	N
R	J	E	O	J	O	R	T	O
D	A	G	Z	U	K	C	A	S
L	I	J	A	G	R	A	G	Z

DEATH
ELIJAH
FLOUR
GATHERING
JAR
JUG
MEAL
OIL
SON
STICKS
WIDOW
ZAREPHATH

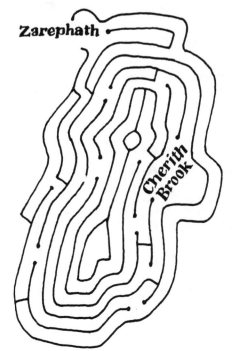

Zarephath

Cherith Brook

The Lord, he is God! The Lord, he is God!

(1 Kings 18:39)

Unscramble this verse:

——— ——— ——— ——— ——— ———— ——— ————

WHO NOLG LIWL OUY VEWAR TEENWBE OWT SPONNIIO ?

Now find it in 1 Kings 18

Word search

ALTAR	MOUNT	SWORDS
BAAL	PROPHETS	TRENCH
BULL	SACRIFICE	WATER
CARMEL	SHOUT	WOOD
ELIJAH	SPEARS	
FIRE	STONES	

M	S	E	N	O	T	S	C	F	I
O	E	M	O	U	N	T	A	B	L
U	L	C	H	E	L	E	R	I	F
N	I	S	I	S	B	H	M	L	A
H	J	L	R	F	W	P	E	L	L
C	A	A	B	A	I	O	L	U	T
N	H	A	D	C	E	R	R	B	A
E	S	B	W	O	R	P	C	D	R
R	O	S	T	U	O	H	S	A	S
T	E	R	E	T	A	W	J	A	S

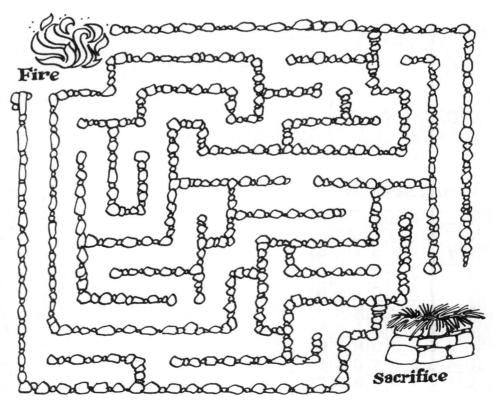

Fire

Sacrifice

Look the story up in 1 Kings 19

Earthquake

Wind

Fire

Gentle Whisper

We think Mount Horeb is the same place as Mount Sinai.

After the fire came a gentle whisper

(1 Kings 19:12)

Remember!
- Even Elijah became afraid and depressed.
- God usually speaks in a gentle whisper.

Word search

ANGEL	DRINK	FIRE	WHISPER
BREAD	EARTHQUAKE	GENTLE	WIND
CAVE	EAT	SINAI	
DIE	ELIJAH	TREE	

D	A	E	R	B	G	E	N	T	L	E	V	E	T
T	R	E	K	A	U	Q	H	T	R	A	E	V	I
A	H	D	R	E	W	H	I	S	P	E	R	A	N
E	H	A	J	I	L	E	D	K	R	K	N	C	T
L	E	G	N	A	F	N	R	T	E	I	D	H	G
	D	R	I	N	K	U	Q	S					

Map labels: Zarephath, Damascus, Mt Carmel, Jezreel, Cherith Brook, Great Sea (Mediterranean), ISRAEL, JUDAH, Beersheba, 50 miles, DESERT, Mt. Sinai

Join up Elijah's route

Zarephath
Mount Carmel
Jezreel
Beersheba
Mount Sinai
Damascus

Read 2 Kings 5

Naaman's Wife's Servant

(God can use you too!)

Help Naaman find Elisha's House

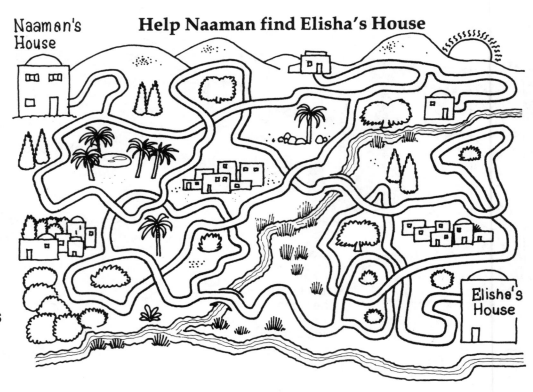

Naaman's House

Elisha's House

Word search

E	C	N	S	F	L	E	S	H
D	O	U	A	L	S	G	E	G
A	Y	M	R	A	G	E	V	I
J	Z	I	E	E	M	H	E	F
O	G	S	E	R	V	A	N	T
R	I	V	E	R	K	Z	N	E
D	O	G	A	H	S	I	L	E
A	I	S	R	A	E	L	N	O
N	T	E	H	P	O	R	P	G

ARMY	ISRAEL
CURE	JORDAN
DISEASE	KING
ELISHA	NAAMAN
FLESH	PROPHET
GEHAZI	RAGE
GIFT	RIVER
GIRL	SERVANT
GOD	SEVEN

Can you make 10 or more words from SERVANT ?

You will find this story in 2 Kings 6:8-23

God is rich in mercy (Ephesians 2:4)

Word search

C	H	A	I	R	O	T	S	E	N
S	I	T	E	L	I	S	H	A	D
T	S	S	H	A	E	L	H	I	R
O	F	E	A	S	T	T	S	F	I
I	O	R	N	M	O	R	E	M	N
R	O	V	K	D	A	A	E	G	K
A	D	A	I	E	N	R	N	G	I
H	S	N	L	M	C	I	I	L	N
C	A	T	O	Y	K	E	L	A	G
H	L	M	E	R	M	A	R	B	I

BLINDNESS
CHARIOTS
DOTHAN
DRINKING
ELISHA
FEAST
FOOD
ISRAEL
KING
MERCY
SAMARIA
SERVANT

Fill in these soldiers' faces and give them some food

Praise the Lord – his love is eternal!

(2 Chronicles 20:21)

Help Jehoshaphat and his people get to a look-out in the desert

You will find this story in 2 Chronicles 20

Give thanks to the Lord! His love lasts for ever!

Start

AMMON
ARMY
ENEMY
EDOM
FAST
JAHAZIEL
JEHOSHAPHAT
JERUSALEM
LOOT
MOAB
PRAYED
PEACE
SINGING
TEMPLE
TRUMPETS

Word search

M	O	B	S	E	L	P	M	E	T
F	A	D	O	M	E	O	S	T	R
T	R	M	B	E	R	S	O	A	U
Z	I	A	S	F	C	E	P	T	M
N	O	N	O	M	M	A	J	A	P
M	L	E	F	F	H	I	E	H	E
L	E	I	Z	A	H	A	J	P	T
P	H	L	I	S	I	N	G	A	S
Y	R	A	A	T	O	E	H	H	O
A	E	R	N	S	J	I	D	S	U
P	M	N	Y	E	U	T	E	O	P
Y	M	E	N	E	J	R	E	H	M
P	R	A	Y	E	D	S	E	E	T
M	M	O	N	E	C	E	A	J	E
E	G	N	I	G	N	I	S	Z	D

Look up Esther 4:14

1. The Banquet
Queen Vashti refuses to come to the King.

2. 12 months later — Esther chosen to be Queen.

3. Two men plot to kill the King.
Mordecai warns King.

4. Haman becomes P.M.
People bow down to him except…

5. Mordecai

6. Law passed that all Jews were to be killed.

7. Mordecai tells Esther

8. 1 2 3
3 days and nights of fasting.

Queen Esther was frightened to approach the King.

9. The King holds out the sceptre to Esther.

10. QUEEN KING HAMAN
Dinner for three 1.

11. Gallows prepared for ? Mordecai.

12. QUEEN KING HAMAN
Dinner for three 2.

13. Haman hanged.
Jews freed!

Try and find a crown hidden in each picture

Word search

BANQUET	JEWS	QUEEN
COURAGE	LAW	SCEPTRE
ESTHER	MORDECAI	VASHTI
FAST	PERSIA	WINE
HAMAN	PLOT	XERXES

T	S	A	F	Q	U	L	I	A	N
R	E	S	E	U	G	A	T	R	E
W	X	W	C	E	C	W	H	A	G
I	R	E	I	E	Q	U	S	E	A
X	E	J	D	N	P	E	A	S	R
N	X	R	H	L	E	T	V	T	U
A	O	E	O	N	R	A	R	H	O
M	E	T	I	O	S	T	C	E	C
H	A	M	A	N	I	E	I	R	E
T	E	U	Q	N	A	B	N	A	B

Read the story in Daniel 1

Draw the faces of Daniel and his friends

| DANIEL | SHADRACH | MESHACH | ABEDNEGO |

Can you fit these words in the boxes?

3 LETTERS
PEA

4 LETTERS
BEAN
LEEK

6 LETTERS
CARROT
CELERY
POTATO
RADISH

7 LETTERS
LETTUCE
PARSNIP
SPINACH

8 LETTERS
BROCCOLI
CUCUMBER

11 LETTERS
CAULIFLOWER

Put a ring around those foods Daniel and his friends were allowed to eat

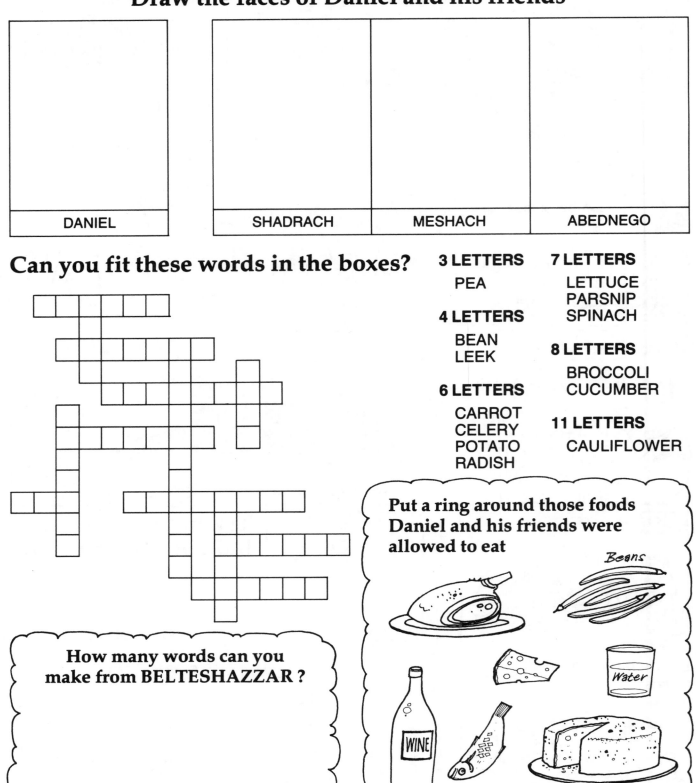

Beans

Water

WINE

How many words can you make from BELTESHAZZAR ?

Say NO to doing wrong

The fiery furnace

Read the story in Daniel 3

Jesus said: "I will be with you always." (Matthew 28:20)

Word search

H	D	E	N	D	C	G	W
C	T	D	W	G	O	O	O
A	G	O	K	I	N	G	R
R	B	M	H	N	E	L	S
D	W	E	R	I	F	C	H
A	C	S	D	R	E	D	I
H	L	H	S	N	U	L	P
S	T	A	T	U	E	O	G
A	H	C	F	T	E	G	F
S	E	H	T	O	L	C	O

ABEDNEGO
BOW
CLOTHES
FIRE
FOUR
GOD
GOLD
HOT
KING
MESHACH
SHADRACH
STATUE
WORSHIP

Which are the odd ones out?

Will you be the odd one out if necessary and still worship God?

Read the story in Daniel 4

Do not be proud

(Romans 12:16)

Help King Neb find his palace

Word search

ANIMALS
BIRDS
CHOP
DANIEL
DEW
DREAM
FRUIT
GRASS
HUMBLE
IRON
NEBUCHADNEZZAR
PROUD
SEVEN
STUMP
TREE

Read the story in Daniel 5

Belshazzar's Feast

Word search

T	H	E	S	T	V	N	G	O	L	B	D
D	I	V	I	S	I	O	N	S	E	A	W
F	R	E	A	T	P	K	I	L	N	R	E
W	E	I	G	H	T	U	S	I	I	T	I
A	H	A	N	D	I	H	C	T	Z	S	T
W	A	S	T	K	A	G	I	A	Z	A	H
L	L	Z	O	Z	I	N	U	M	B	E	R
T	L	O	Z	L	G	N	I	K	S	F	S
I	N	A	G	D	L	O	G	E	I	O	N
L	R	M	W	E	I	K	I	N	L	S	T

BELSHAZZAR	FEAST	NUMBER
CUPS	GOLD	WALL
DANIEL	HAND	WEIGHT
DIVISIONS	KING	WRITING
DRINKING		

Number Number Weight Divisions

What will make these balance?

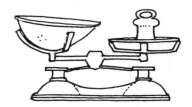

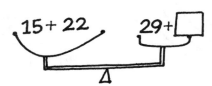

15 + 22   29 + ☐

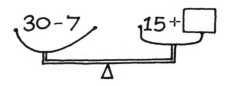

30 − 7   15 + ☐

He prayed to God three times a day

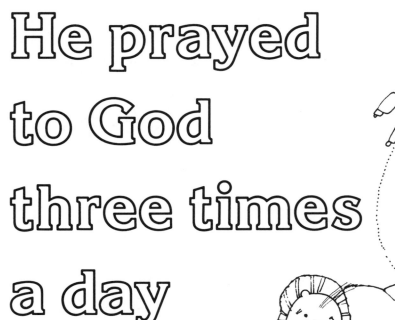

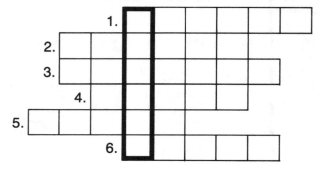

Read the story in Daniel 6

Help Daniel find his way out of the lions den

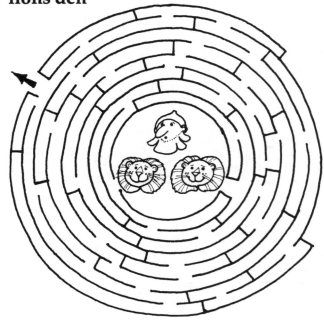

Find the words from the verses in the story and write the letters in the boxes:

1. The King's name: verse 1
2. Daniel did this 3 times a day: verse 10
3. These opened towards Jerusalem: verse 10
4. The King spent a sleepless one: verse 18
5. This shut the lion's mouth: verse 22
6. Daniel was rescued from the: verse 22

You will find this story in the book of Jonah in the Old Testament

Obey the Lord your God

(Deuteronomy 27:10)

Word search

FISH	NINEVEH	PRAYED	SORRY
JOPPA	OBEY	SAILORS	STORM
JONAH	PLANT	SEA	WORM

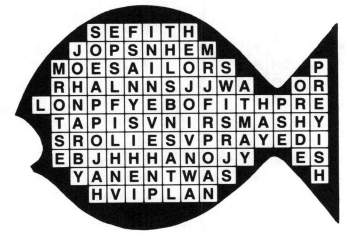

God has asked these Christians
to do a job with him.
Who says 'YES'?   Who says 'NO'?

'NO'   'YES'   'NO'   'YES'

Read Matthew 4:1-11

Put a ring around any of these temptations you have had

Stealing

Swearing

Being Greedy

Lying

Being Lazy

Cheating

Being Rude

Being Proud

Fighting

Jump off

All this could be mine

Turn these stones into bread

Word search

ANGELS   FORTY   SPIRIT   TEST

BREAD   HUNGRY   STONES   WORLD

DESERT   JESUS   TEMPLE   WORSHIP

DEVIL   MOUNTAIN   TEMPTED

Read this story in
Matthew 14:13-21

It's also in
Mark 6
Luke 9
John 6

Jesus makes a lot out of a little given to him

Can you fit these words into the boxes?

3 LETTERS
BOY
SEA
TWO

4 LETTERS
FISH
FIVE

5 LETTERS
BREAD
GRASS

6 LETTERS
CROWDS
LOAVES
PEOPLE
TWELVE

7 LETTERS
BASKETS
GALILEE

8 LETTERS
MOUNTAIN

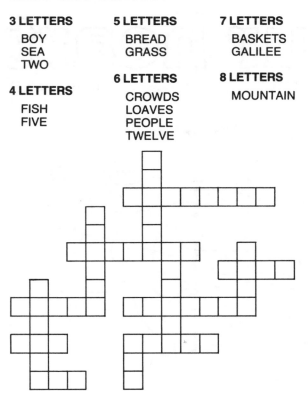

Put a circle around the numbers which are in the story

3   24   100

16   5,000   2

12   5

7   10

1,000   8   4

Find this story in Matthew 14:22-32

Trust in the Lord with all your heart

(Proverbs 3:5)

Word search

DOUBT	FORGIVEN	WAVES
FAITH	PETER	WATER
FEAR	ROCK	WET
FEET	WALK	

G	K	T	E	R	V	B	E	C	D
E	F	A	I	T	H	G	K	W	T
P	E	F	O	W	K	F	E	A	R
K	C	F	T	A	B	O	U	V	O
Y	T	P	E	T	E	R	S	E	B
W	A	E	N	E	U	G	K	S	T
N	V	R	A	R	T	I	L	R	B
B	P	O	T	B	S	V	A	D	U
K	T	C	D	E	T	E	W	E	O
E	N	K	W	A	B	N	U	O	D

Which hand helps Peter?

He will go to look for the one that wandered off (Matthew 18:12)

Help the shepherd find the lamb

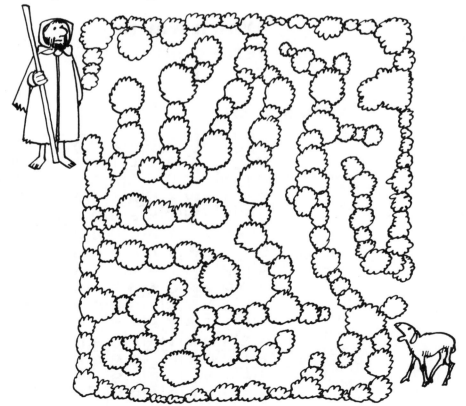

Look up John 1:17. Who brought grace and truth? _____ _____

Word search

F	R	U	O	V	A	F	D	R	S
O	K	I	N	T	O	G	R	E	H
N	E	I	S	U	R	L	A	R	E
D	H	O	N	A	V	R	H	E	P
O	L	D	C	D	C	E	P	Y	H
G	A	E	C	H	N	R	E	A	E
D	M	K	I	N	D	E	H	R	R
E	B	N	U	F	N	D	S	T	D
S	G	R	E	P	E	E	H	S	N
D	E	V	R	E	S	E	D	N	U

FAVOUR	LOST
FIELD	SEARCHING
FOUND	SHEEP
GRACE	SHEPHERD
KINDNESS	STRAY
LAMB	UNDESERVED

Read the story in Matthew 21

King of Kings!

Which way to Jerusalem? ☐

Word search

How many faces? ☐

BRANCHES
COLT
DISCIPLES
DONKEY
DOOR
HOUSE
INSTRUCTION
JERUSALEM
MASTER
PALM
PEOPLE
ROAD
SHOUT
SUNDAY
TWO
UNTIE
VILLAGE

H	U	T	R	J	S	G	M	X	H	W	S	I	D
O	S	H	E	G	A	L	L	I	V	I	E	N	O
U	G	S	T	C	S	R	A	W	T	R	L	S	N
S	H	Y	S	V	A	H	A	E	O	A	P	T	K
E	B	R	A	N	C	H	E	S	D	B	I	R	E
A	S	N	M	D	Y	A	D	N	U	S	C	U	Y
S	P	E	L	E	T	A	L	H	C	D	S	C	L
A	E	P	A	C	L	R	A	L	Y	A	I	T	I
N	O	M	P	R	O	A	D	X	Z	D	D	I	N
N	P	O	N	Y	C	V	S	H	O	U	T	O	G
T	L	I	T	A	Y	E	U	U	M	O	O	N	H
T	H	E	R	M	M	I	A	A	U	R	O	O	D
T	I	P	D	T	L	L	O	M	A	E	T	W	T
H	P	G	N	A	Y	P	Q	S	T	R	J	U	W
H	E	U	S	O	O	D	R	M	Y	E	Y	O	O

Find this story in Matthew 25

Be Ready

Word search

ASLEEP
BRIDEGROOM
CONTAINERS
CRY
FIVE
FOOLISH
FULL
GIRLS
KINGDOM
LAMPS

LATE
MEET
MIDNIGHT
OIL
READY
SHOP
TEN
TRIMMED
WEDDING
WISE

A	S	L	E	E	V	I	F	E	O	I
E	H	F	A	T	E	O	W	P	Y	B
V	O	C	U	A	O	N	E	T	R	T
S	P	M	A	L	I	E	D	I	C	R
I	M	G	I	R	L	S	D	G	O	I
W	I	S	E	S	T	E	I	K	Y	M
I	H	A	A	E	G	L	N	I	D	M
E	D	D	E	R	S	I	G	N	A	E
T	R	M	O	D	G	N	I	K	E	D
S	C	O	N	T	A	I	N	E	R	S
E	M	I	D	N	I	G	H	T	E	D

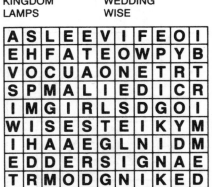

How many wise bridesmaids?

How many foolish bridesmaids?

How many cups of wine?

Find Judas' path to the money

Break the code to find out what Jesus said

1	2	3	4	5	6	7	8	9	10
B	D	H	I	L	M	O	S	T	Y

_ _ _ _   _ _   _ _
9 3 4 8   4 8   6 10

_ _ _ _   _ _ _ _
1 7 2 10   9 3 4 8

_ _   _ _   _ _ _ _ _
4 8   6 10   1 5 7 7 2

(Matthew 26:26-30)

Jesus is killed

1 Jesus is Betrayed
Matthew 26:14

_ _ _ _ _ _   betrayed Jesus.

2 The Lord's Supper
Matthew 26:26-30

Jesus gave His disciples

_ _ _ _ _ _   and   _ _ _ _ _

3 Jesus is Crucified
Matthew 27:32-44

The notice above Jesus' head said:

_ _ _ _ _ _ _ _   _ _ _ _ _ _ _ _ _

_ _ _   _ _ _ _ _   _ _

_ _ _ _   _ _ _ _ _

Word search

ASLEEP	CROSS	JESUS	PRAYER
BLOOD	CRUCIFIXION	JUDAS	SOLDIERS
BODY	DISCIPLES	PALMS	WINE
BREAD	DONKEY	PASSOVER	
CALVARY	JERUSALEM	PILATE	

A	S	E	V	E	P	A	L	M	S	J	S	U	S	O	B
N	E	Y	O	X	E	I	O	N	S	A	T	H	V	I	P
D	I	S	C	Y	E	K	N	O	D	C	D	C	O	O	R
B	P	I	M	E	L	A	S	U	R	E	J	A	E	Y	A
E	L	E	S	U	S	E	J	U	O	X	S	L	E	P	S
Y	D	O	S	E	A	U	C	K	I	R	R	V	S	R	U
O	O	N	O	J	P	I	L	A	T	E	E	A	E	A	B
D	E	E	R	D	F	R	S	Y	E	V	I	R	L	Y	D
D	I	S	C	I	P	L	E	S	B	O	D	Y	W	E	U
E	N	O	X	D	R	E	V	O	S	S	L	K	I	R	S
E	N	I	W	E	K	N	O	D	E	S	O	R	E	Y	J
D	O	P	L	E	S	Y	E	C	E	A	S	O	N	E	U
N	E	D	A	E	V	L	A	C	T	P	C	R	S	O	S

Jesus is risen

Read the story in Matthew 28

He has risen from the dead (Matthew 28:7)

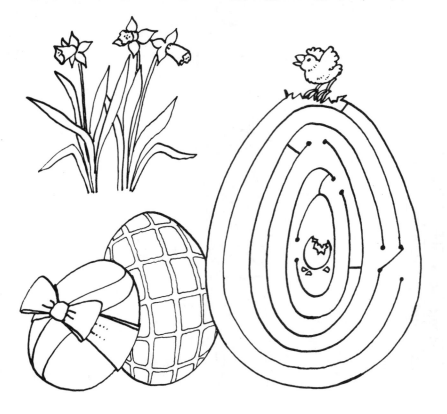

Word search

ALIVE   JOHN   STONE
ANGELS   MAGDALENE   SUNDAY
EASTER   MARY   TOMB
EMPTY   MORNING   WRAPPINGS
GARDENER   PETER
JESUS   RESURRECTION

S	A	N	E	G	N	I	N	R	O	M	A
G	L	D	A	O	S	T	O	V	R	A	L
N	I	E	J	S	U	S	I	E	O	R	V
I	V	O	G	E	N	O	T	S	E	G	E
P	E	R	Y	N	R	S	C	N	B	D	M
P	J	E	T	A	A	Y	E	J	M	A	P
A	E	N	P	E	D	L	R	A	O	L	P
R	S	E	M	H	A	N	R	S	T	H	I
W	R	D	E	D	N	Y	U	O	B	E	N
E	N	R	G	O	T	S	S	S	I	N	G
Y	G	A	R	D	E	P	E	T	E	R	S
A	M	G	E	J	M	O	R	N	S	T	Y

He must become more important while I become less important

(John 3:30)

Circle all the things that WATER does

cleans

keeps you alive

sticks

drowns

talks

quenches thirst

washes

burns

refreshes

jumps

fights

tells jokes

Word search

B	A	L	N	H	O	J	C	T	E	C	S	X	J
S	T	S	U	C	O	L	I	R	A	R	N	O	N
E	H	O	S	T	I	N	Y	M	E	L	H	D	A
D	V	O	L	E	N	A	E	I	L	P	H	S	M
S	Z	O	A	A	W	L	D	Y	L	O	E	H	X
U	E	L	D	A	S	L	S	U	S	T	I	N	A
S	D	R	N	H	O	L	Y	S	P	I	R	I	T
E	O	R	A	S	T	R	I	H	S	I	N	S	H
J	U	I	S	E	Z	I	T	P	A	B	I	E	R
T	R	T	Z	E	O	V	C	T	S	D	A	N	S

BAPTIZE   HONEY   JORDAN   SHIRTS
CAMELS HAIR LOCUSTS   REPENT   TAX MAN
DOVE   JESUS   SANDALS   TURN AWAY
HOLY SPIRIT JOHN   SOLDIERS

The paralysed man healed

Find this story in Mark 2:1-12

Word search

P	L	A	M	E	R	S	H	I	N
W	A	L	K	A	T	T	F	D	E
A	O	R	G	M	I	S	O	B	E
S	I	O	A	A	E	O	R	O	S
T	V	T	F	L	R	O	G	N	E
E	F	O	O	R	Y	R	I	O	D
W	A	H	U	E	M	S	V	O	G
I	A	V	R	E	E	N	E	M	O
D	E	L	E	G	I	V	N	D	V
R	P	E	M	S	O	O	L	E	I
S	A	L	K	S	W	A	M	T	E

DOOR
FAITH
FORGIVEN
FOUR
HOLE
MAT
MEN
PARALYSED
ROOF
SINS
WALK

Fill in the words from this box:

walk	roof	sins	mat

1. The hole was in the __ __ __ __ .

2. The man was lying on a __ __ __ .

3. Jesus said, "Your __ __ __ __ are forgiven."

4. Jesus said, "Pick up your mat and __ __ __ __ ."

You will find this story in Mark 12:41-44 and Luke 21:1-4

God loves a cheerful giver

(2 Corinthians 9:7)

Money in New Testament Times

Jewish	Roman	British
◎ 1 lepton		15p
◎◎ 2 lepta	◎ 1 quadran	30p
	◎◎◎◎ 4 quadrans = ◯ 1 as	£1 - 25
	16 as = ◎ 1 denarius	£20 - 00

A Tithe God's Part

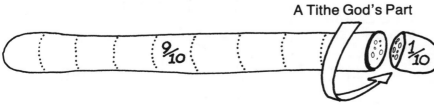

9/10   1/10

Word search

CHEERFUL   PROUD
COINS   RICH
COPPER   SACRIFICE
GIVE   TEMPLE
HUMBLE   TITHE
MONEY   TREASURY
POOR   WIDOW

N	S	L	C	I	N	S	E	E	W
O	A	U	O	D	O	N	V	I	G
T	C	F	E	H	W	I	D	E	R
I	R	R	G	C	M	O	N	E	Y
T	I	E	F	I	W	C	P	L	E
H	F	E	A	R	V	P	O	B	N
E	I	H	E	S	O	E	U	M	O
S	C	C	F	C	U	O	D	U	O
I	E	R	D	U	O	R	P	H	R
P	T	E	M	P	L	E	Y	Y	E

Read the story in Luke 1

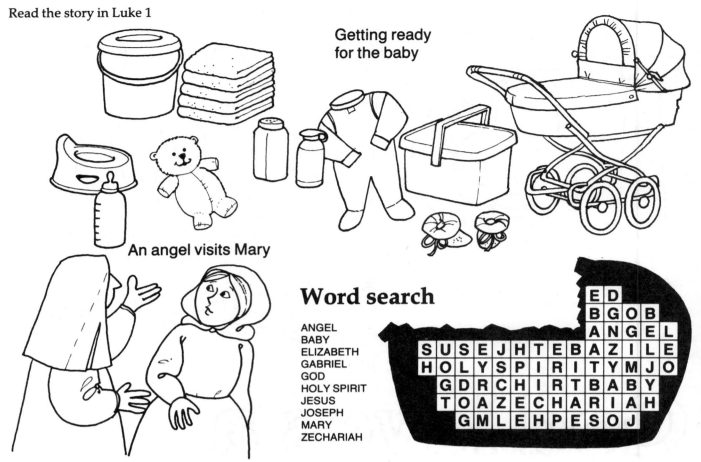

Getting ready for the baby

An angel visits Mary

Word search

ANGEL
BABY
ELIZABETH
GABRIEL
GOD
HOLY SPIRIT
JESUS
JOSEPH
MARY
ZECHARIAH

E	D								
B	G	O	B						
B	A	N	G	E	L				
S	U	S	E	J	H	T	E	B	A	Z	I	L	E
H	O	L	Y	S	P	I	R	I	T	Y	M	J	O
G	D	R	C	H	I	R	T	B	A	B	Y
T	O	A	Z	E	C	H	A	R	I	A	H
G	M	L	E	H	P	E	S	O	J

For there is nothing that God cannot do (Luke 1:37)

Help Mary find Elizabeth by answering the questions correctly

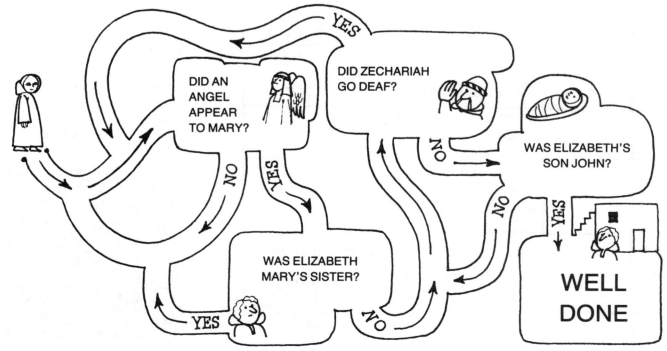

YES

DID AN ANGEL APPEAR TO MARY?

DID ZECHARIAH GO DEAF?

NO

WAS ELIZABETH'S SON JOHN?

NO

YES

NO

YES

WAS ELIZABETH MARY'S SISTER?

WELL DONE

YES

NO

Immanuel – God is with us

(Matthew 1:23)

Find the words on the tree

```
      B I
      N O
    N O S T
      E M H M
      J H L A T A
    M O O R B N R B
    T S Y L S A G I
    A M E H E L H T E B
    J O P O J E S U S R
    H S E H T O L C O O E L
```

CLOTH　INN　JOSEPH　SON
BETHLEHEM　JESUS　MANGER
BIRTH　MARY
STABLE　ROOM

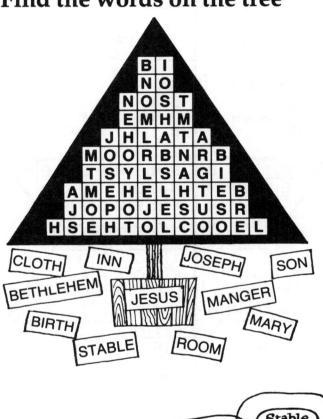

Lead Mary and Joseph to the stable

Read the story in Luke 2 and Matthew 2

We have come to worship him

(Matthew 1:2)

Word search

ANGELS
BETHLEHEM
CHILD
EAST

HEROD
KING
MANGER
MARY

FIELDS
FRANKINCENSE
GIFTS
GOLD

MYRRH
SHEPHERDS
SINGING
STAR

Read the story in Luke 2:22-38

Word search

C	H	I	D	L	N	T	F	T	S	A	N	T	S
J	E	R	U	S	A	L	E	M	U	J	I	E	I
E	E	S	A	N	K	I	O	M	S	E	P	L	M
L	O	S	N	O	G	E	D	O	P	S	A	T	I
U	S	A	U	H	W	L	M	W	E	L	R	K	S
M	D	O	T	S	I	W	E	S	I	M	E	O	N
E	C	H	I	H	D	T	H	A	L	E	N	E	T
L	I	M	C	E	O	S	K	N	A	H	T	S	I
T	A	N	E	O	W	G	H	T	S	I	S	E	W

ANNA	JESUS	TEMPLE
CHILD	PARENTS	THANKS
EIGHT	SIMEON	WIDOW
JERUSALEM		

Help Anna find Simeon and Jesus

Anna

Simeon

Use the code ⌐ = i, ∨ = o etc
to find out what this says:-

Habakkuk 2:3

Read the story in Luke 2:41-52

Jesus grew both in

Put the first letter of the picture in each box

and

and gaining favour with God and men

(Luke 2:52)

Help Mary and Joseph find Jesus in the temple

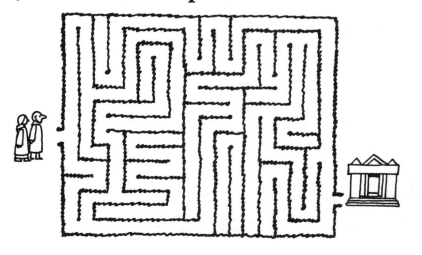

AMAZED
BOY
DAY
FATHERS
HOUSE
JERUSALEM
JESUS
MOTHER
PARENTS
QUESTIONS
TEMPLE
TWELVE
WISDOM
WORRIED

Word search

T	R	M	O	T	H	E	R	M	I
W	O	E	Y	B	L	V	E	S	W
T	H	J	D	O	L	L	W	Q	O
E	E	W	E	Y	A	E	J	U	M
E	M	O	D	S	I	W	S	E	Z
V	O	R	U	Q	U	T	R	S	A
P	A	R	E	N	T	S	E	T	M
L	E	I	E	S	U	O	H	I	A
J	T	E	M	P	L	E	T	O	J
Y	A	D	E	Z	A	M	A	N	E
E	M	O	D	H	T	A	F	S	H

Read the story in Luke 5:1-11

There are 6 fish hidden in the picture. Can you find them?

They left everything and followed Jesus

(Luke 5:11)

See if you can fit in the names of the disciples:-

ANDREW	JAMES	MATTHEW	SIMON
BARTHOLOMEW	JOHN	PETER	THADDAEUS
JAMES	JUDAS	PHILIP	THOMAS

These names are listed in Matthew 10:2-4

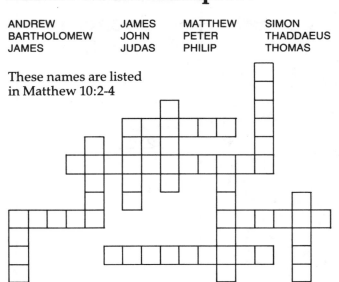

Write down the names of your best friends

The Bible tells us to be careful in choosing our friends.

The centurion and his servant

Luke 7:1-10

Try and find these words in the puzzle

N	Q	S	D	N	E	I	R	F
D	O	Z	A	J	W	O	F	O
E	H	I	D	E	O	E	T	O
Z	T	O	R	S	R	L	N	R
A	I	O	O	U	H	E	A	L
M	A	M	W	S	T	P	V	P
A	F	V	O	B	Y	N	R	C
W	O	R	T	H	Y	I	E	A
O	S	E	S	U	O	H	S	C

AMAZED
CENTURION
FAITH
FRIENDS
HEAL
HOUSE
JESUS
ROOF
SERVANT
WORD
WORTHY

Help the centurion's friends find Jesus

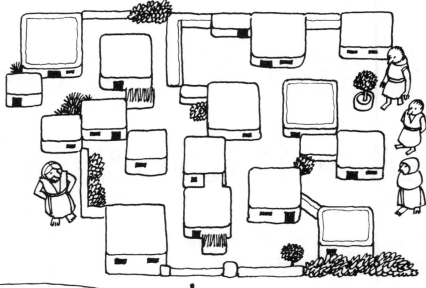

Please help me to remember I can pray for my friends where ever they are.

Friends to pray for:-

1. _____

2. _____

3. _____

4. _____

5. _____

Jairus and his daughter

Luke 8:40-56

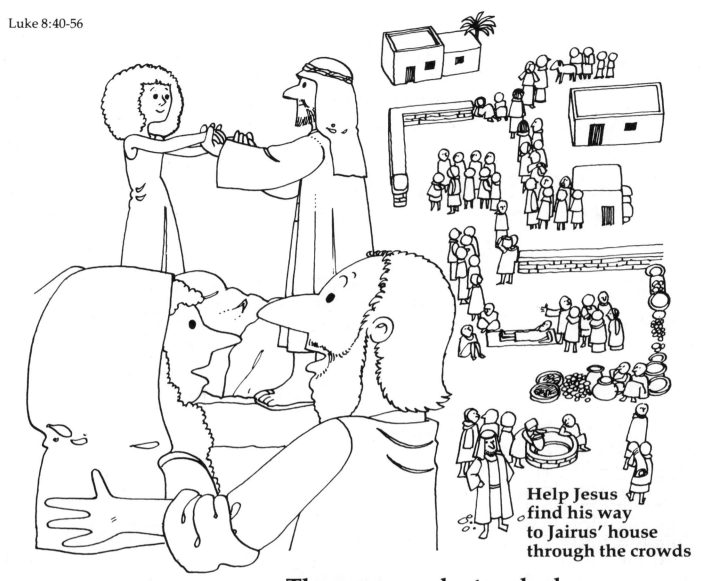

Help Jesus find his way to Jairus' house through the crowds

Word search

ASLEEP   HAND   MOTHER
BELIEVE   HEALED   MOURNING
DAUGHTER HOUSE   RULER
DEAD   JAIRUS   SYNAGOGUE
EAT   JESUS

A	S	B	D	A	E	D	B	L	E	S
H	T	A	E	S	J	E	S	S	U	D
A	A	L	I	L	A	L	E	E	A	E
D	E	S	U	R	I	A	J	U	S	N
N	M	Y	E	V	R	E	G	O	L	U
N	O	N	E	E	S	H	V	R	E	O
I	H	A	P	U	T	S	L	E	E	P
D	T	G	S	E	S	J	U	H	P	O
N	R	O	R	U	L	E	R	T	T	H
A	E	G	N	I	N	R	U	O	M	E
H	O	U	S	E	A	U	G	M	H	O
B	I	E	V	E	L	N	I	N	G	S

The woman who touched Jesus' cloak

Number these pictures in the correct order

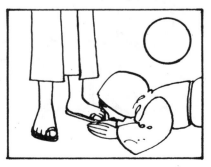

Find this story in Luke 8

The seed is like the word of God

The Path	Rocky Ground
The message taken away	Time of testing
The weeds and thorns	The Good Soil
Worries and Riches	Good Fruit

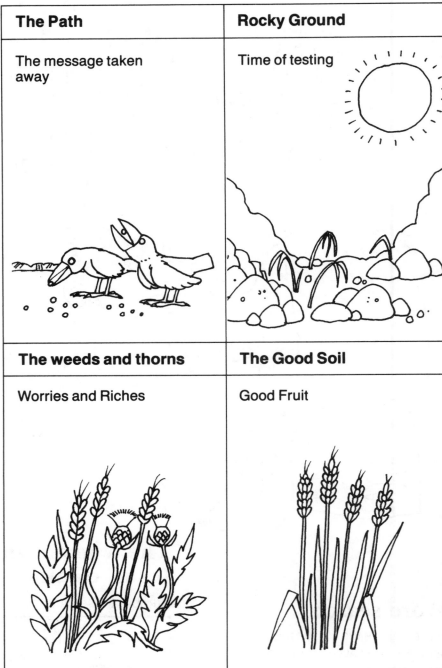

Word search

T	U	N	S	T	N	A	L	P
E	O	W	D	R	U	I	S	A
S	D	E	E	S	S	D	E	T
E	N	E	E	O	R	E	T	H
G	U	N	W	I	B	V	R	S
F	O	E	B	L	D	I	O	O
R	R	O	K	Y	C	L	C	W
U	G	W	D	H	B	F	K	N
I	U	I	E	E	S	R	Y	E
T	I	S	N	R	O	H	T	D

BIRDS   PATH   SOIL
DEVIL   PLANTS   SOWER
FRUIT   RICHES   THORNS
GOOD   ROCKY   WEEDS
GROUND   SEEDS

Which sort of ground are you?

Read this story in Luke 8

Even the winds and waves obey him (Matthew 8:27)

Word search

ASLEEP
BOAT
CALM
DISCIPLES
FAITH
JESUS
LAKE

OBEY
QUIET
SIDE
STILL
STORM
WAVES
WIND

Draw a circle around those things you might find at the sea-side

Read the story in Luke 10:25-37

Love your neighbour as you love yourself

(Luke 10:27)

Cut out the shapes and complete the sentences by matching them together

There once was a man who went from...

The man fell into the hands of robbers who...

A priest saw the man and...

A Levite saw the man and...

A Samaritan saw the man and...

The Samaritan put the man on a donkey and...

passed by on the other side.

took pity on him and bandaged his wounds.

beat him up and left him.

took him to an inn and paid for the man and said he would come back the next day.

Jerusalem to Jericho.

he too passed on the other side.

Word search

L	P	R	I	E	S	T	I	M	O
N	O	E	A	R	A	S	E	R	R
O	L	V	N	A	M	L	T	U	P
H	I	N	E	C	A	S	I	O	S
C	I	L	V	S	R	R	V	B	V
I	J	E	U	M	I	E	E	H	E
R	N	R	I	E	T	B	L	G	I
E	E	R	O	B	A	B	O	I	V
J	O	Y	E	K	N	O	D	E	A
D	O	N	K	Y	E	R	A	N	U

CARE　　　　　JERICHO
DONKEY　　　JERUSALEM
INN　　　　　　OIL
LEVITE　　　　PRIEST
LOVE　　　　　ROBBERS
MAN　　　　　SAMARITAN
NEIGHBOUR

The good father

Story found in Luke 15:11-32

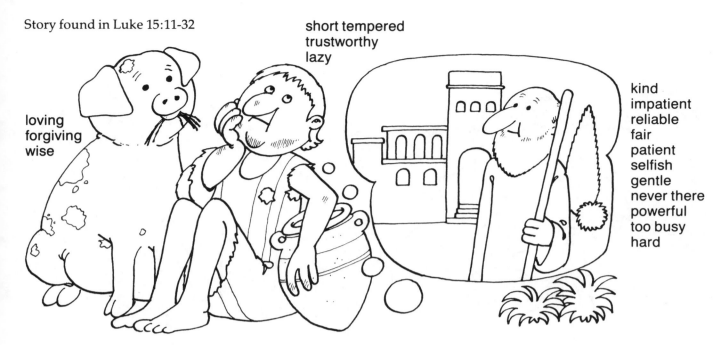

short tempered
trustworthy
lazy

loving
forgiving
wise

kind
impatient
reliable
fair
patient
selfish
gentle
never there
powerful
too busy
hard

The Lord is gracious and compassionate, slow to anger and rich in love (Psalm 145:8)

Word search

BROTHER   OLDER   SON
CELEBRATE PIGS   SORRY
FATHER   PROPERTY   WASTED
FORGIVE   SERVANTS   YOUNGER

O	R	E	G	N	U	O	Y	P	I
B	E	F	E	V	I	G	R	O	F
R	H	A	S	N	S	E	R	S	G
O	T	H	T	O	H	T	O	N	F
T	O	E	N	T	Y	U	S	A	R
Y	R	W	A	S	T	E	D	E	R
P	B	F	V	O	U	S	D	T	Y
E	T	A	R	B	E	L	E	C	G
Y	T	R	E	P	O	R	P	E	E
A	B	L	S	G	I	P	E	C	R

Help the younger son find his way home from the pigs

Tick any words on this sheet which describe a good father. How many can you find? ☐

Read the story in Luke 17:11-18

And be thankful (Colossians 3:15)

Word search

B	E	T	H	A	N	K	F	C	U	L	B
E	T	H	A	T	N	K	L	N	F	R	J
L	B	S	R	E	P	E	L	T	E	E	H
A	N	S	K	N	A	H	T	N	R	M	K
F	U	L	B	N	E	T	G	U	T	H	J
A	N	K	F	U	D	I	S	E	A	S	E
L	B	D	E	H	E	A	L	E	D	N	S
H	A	N	K	R	L	F	Y	T	I	P	U
F	U	L	O	E	B	E	T	N	H	A	S
N	K	F	M	P	R	I	E	S	T	S	F

CLEAN
DISEASE
FAITH
FOREIGNER
HEALED
JERUSALEM
JESUS
LEPERS
MEN
NINE
PITY
PRIESTS
TEN
THANKS

Thank you Lord for:

_____

_____

_____

_____

_____

Read the story in Luke 19:1-10

Salvation is found in no one else. For there is no other name under heaven given to men by which we must be saved

(Acts 4:12)

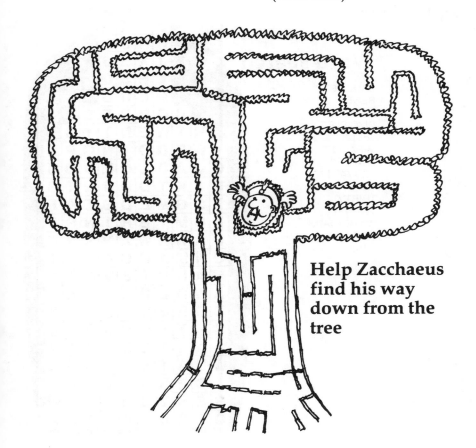

Help Zacchaeus find his way down from the tree

Word search

CHIEF	JESUS	SYCAMORE
COLLECTOR	JOY	TAX
CROWD	LITTLE	TREE
FOUR	POOR	ZACCHAEUS
HOUSE	RICH	
JERICHO	SALVATION	

F	S	U	S	E	J	S	A	L	V	A
H	O	U	S	F	E	I	H	C	L	T
N	C	U	E	I	R	H	S	N	I	O
S	O	Y	R	C	I	O	U	E	T	P
H	L	I	R	Y	C	E	E	R	T	R
J	L	U	T	O	H	J	A	O	L	O
S	E	S	E	A	O	N	H	M	E	X
H	C	I	R	Y	V	P	C	A	T	A
Z	T	A	X	S	U	L	C	C	A	Z
A	O	L	I	T	M	O	A	Y	J	E
C	R	O	W	D	R	E	Z	S	R	I

Read this story in John 2

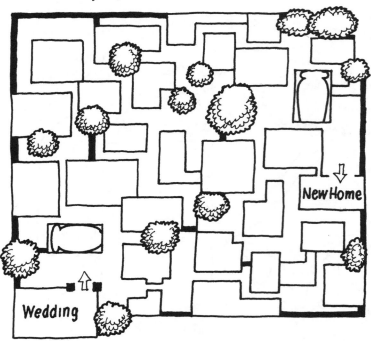

Follow the route through the village to the couple's new home

Do whatever he tells you

(John 2:5)

See if you can find six water jars on this page

Word search

BANQUET
BEST
CANA
DISCIPLES
JESUS
MIRACLES
MOTHER
SERVANTS
SIX
THIRTY
TWENTY
WATER JARS
WEDDING
WINE

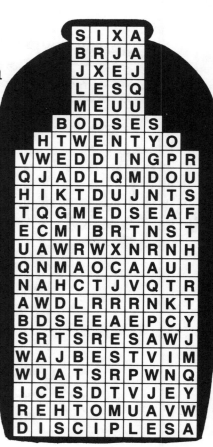

Find this story in John 9

I was blind

but now I see

(John 9:25)

Word search

T	H	G	I	S	Y	U	D	F
A	S	N	I	S	E	I	F	S
B	L	I	N	D	U	E	A	E
L	O	G	L	O	Y	S	C	Y
I	O	G	B	O	R	N	E	E
N	P	E	H	S	A	W	H	J
B	O	B	T	D	U	M	E	S

BEGGING

BLIND

BORN

EYES

FACE

JESUS

MUD

POOL

SEE

SIGHT

SILOAM

SINS

WASH

Use your eyes and count how many naughty children there are here ☐

Read the story in John 12:1-8

The perfume filled the house

(John 12:3)

Tick the smells you like

- [ ] Fish and Chips
- [ ] After Shave
- [ ] Petrol
- [ ] Smoke
- [ ] Roses
- [ ] The Sea
- [ ] Banana
- [ ] Burnt Toast

Word search

BETHANY	MONEY
DINNER	NARD
FEET	PERFUME
HAIR	POOR
HOUSE	POURED
JESUS	SMELL
LAZARUS	SOLD
MARTHA	TABLE
MARY	WIPED

S	U	S	E	J	E	E	L	D	L	M
M	E	P	S	S	M	A	R	Y	A	O
E	O	O	U	U	Z	A	H	R	Y	N
L	L	O	F	A	N	L	R	N	A	E
D	H	R	R	E	L	B	A	T	H	Y
E	E	U	F	E	E	H	E	N	H	Z
P	S	O	M	T	T	T	S	A	W	A
I	H	S	R	E	N	N	I	D	I	L
W	T	E	B	D	E	R	U	O	P	E

Are you mean or generous with your giving?

Be extravagant giving to God

Lazarus back to life

Spot the 10 differences:

Find this story in John 11

Jesus said:-

I am the

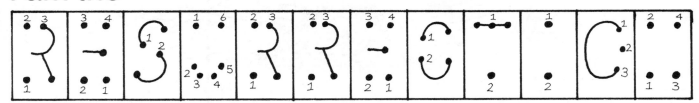

and the

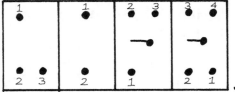

John 11:25

Draw in the faces of the people when they saw Lazarus come out of the tomb

Who were Lazarus' sisters?

M _ _ _ _ and M _ _ _ _ _ _

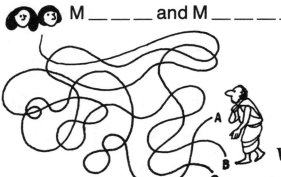

Which way? ☐

Who else was raised from the dead? _ _ _ _ _ _ _

Read the story in John 21:1-19

Take care of my sheep (John 21:16)

1. The disciples went fishing with ___ ___ ___ ___ ___   v.3
2. How many went fishing? ___ ___ ___ ___   v.2
3. They fished from a ___ ___ ___ ___   v.3
4. They fished with a ___ ___ ___   v.6
5. They fished until early ___ ___ ___ ___ ___ ___   v.4

6. They caught no ___ ___ ___ ___   v.5
7. The man on the shore was ___ ___ ___ ___ ___   v.4

8. They could see a charcoal ___ ___ ___ ___   v.9
9. Peter heard it was the ___ ___ ___ ___   v.7
10. They had fish and ___ ___ ___ ___ ___   v.9
11. The net was full of ___ ___   fish.   v.11
12. Peter's other name was ___ ___ ___ ___ ___   v.15
13. Jesus asked, "Do you ___ ___ ___ ___   me?"   v.16
14. Jesus said, "Take care of my ___ ___ ___ ___ ___   v.16
15. This is in the Book of ___ ___ ___ ___

Which fishing rod catches the fish?

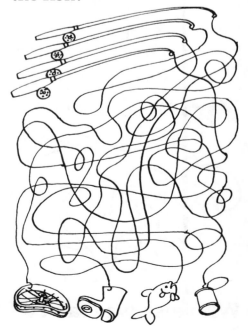

There are many rooms in my Father's house and I am going to prepare a place for you

(John 14:2)

Jesus left his eleven close friends to carry out his work.

Judas was dead, so they chose Matthias to take his place.

Unjumble the names of the 12 men

Here are the 12 — finish drawing them.

1. PREET
2. MAJES
3. HONJ
4. WREAND
5. HIPPIL
6. WEBROTHAMLO
7. AWTHMET
8. MOTASH
9. SMEAJ
10. DUTHSEAD
11. NOIMS
12. THAMAIST

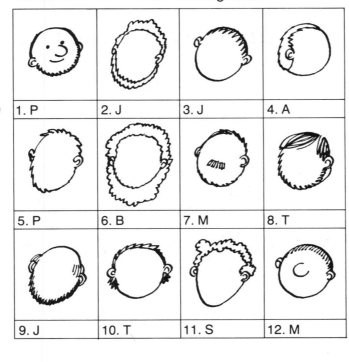

1. P   2. J   3. J   4. A

5. P   6. B   7. M   8. T

9. J   10. T   11. S   12. M

Word search

APOSTLES	HOUSE	SPIRIT
ASCENSION	JESUS	WAIT
CLOUD	PREPARE	WATCHED
HEAVEN	ROOMS	
HOLY	SKY	

S	P	Y	I	N	T	L	A	N	T	J	E
U	E	P	L	A	S	I	E	C	S	E	T
H	W	E	N	O	I	S	N	E	C	S	A
V	A	S	C	L	H	E	C	W	E	U	S
P	T	Y	R	O	S	P	E	L	T	S	O
S	C	K	U	E	M	J	T	M	O	E	U
K	H	S	N	C	O	S	H	A	C	U	T
P	E	R	E	I	O	T	C	W	E	I	D
E	D	O	V	P	R	E	P	A	R	E	D
W	A	T	A	E	S	C	A	I	T	S	L
A	P	O	E	S	T	L	P	T	D	E	W
S	C	E	H	C	O	S	T	L	E	S	A

Pentecost

Find this story in Acts 2

5
6
7
8
9
10
Hours

AFRAID ——► then ——► BRAVE

The Holy Spirit helps us to:

Tell Others
Understand the Bible
Know what to do
Be Joyful

Word search

H	A	H	E	L	P	E	R	D
E	G	O	J	M	P	S	V	E
A	F	L	A	M	E	S	V	Y
V	B	Y	E	H	K	A	N	Q
E	T	S	W	Z	R	C	F	P
N	I	P	L	B	O	O	R	R
U	X	I	A	D	G	J	O	O
J	E	R	U	S	A	L	E	M
E	M	I	P	S	F	E	V	I
S	Y	T	B	E	R	H	K	S
U	N	Q	T	I	A	W	Z	E
S	C	F	F	I	I	L	O	R
U	X	W	I	N	D	A	D	G

AFRAID
BRAVE
FIRE
FLAMES
HEAVEN
HELPER
HOLY SPIRIT
JERUSALEM
JESUS
PROMISE
ROOM
WIND

Read this story in Acts 3

Healed

Can you make at least 10 words from BEAUTIFUL ?

Can you pair up these feet?

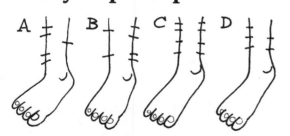

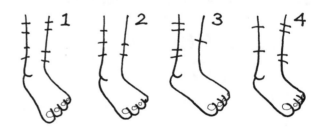

Word search

H	T	G	N	E	R	T	S	H	O	A
T	W	A	L	K	E	D	P	G	B	N
J	M	N	M	P	R	G	R	E	E	K
E	M	S	E	L	K	N	A	G	G	L
S	P	E	T	E	R	U	Y	T	G	Y
U	J	H	E	H	T	E	E	H	E	E
S	L	R	E	I	H	M	R	R	D	N
W	H	S	F	A	P	A	J	E	H	O
T	W	U	N	L	S	L	E	O	D	M
A	L	D	E	P	M	U	J	O	W	B
P	R	A	I	S	I	N	G	G	E	B

ANKLES	LAME
BEAUTIFUL	MONEY
BEGGED	NAME
FEET	PETER
GATE	PRAISING
GOD	PRAYER
HAND	STRENGTH
HELP	TEMPLE
JESUS	THREE
JOHN	WALKED
JUMPED	

Acts 5:1-12

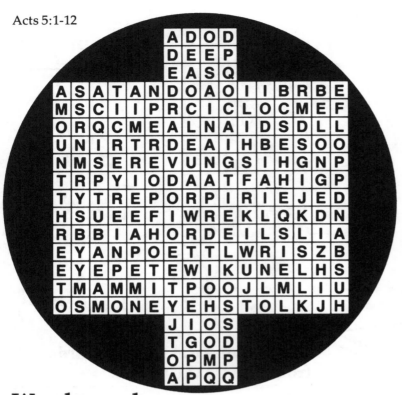

AMOUNT	GOD	SAPPHIRA
ANANIAS	HOURS	SATAN
APOSTLES	HUSBAND	SHARED
BELONGED	LIED	SOLD
BURIED	MONEY	TERRIFIED
CARRY	PETER	THREE
DEAD	PROPERTY	WIFE

Word search

If Sapphira and Ananias sold the field for 150 pounds and only gave in 82 how much money would they have kept?

Answer = ☐

Don't lie: God sees everything

Spot the 7 differences

How many words can you make from the name Sapphira?

How many words can you make from the name Ananias?

Read this story in Acts 7:54-60

His Spirit fills us with

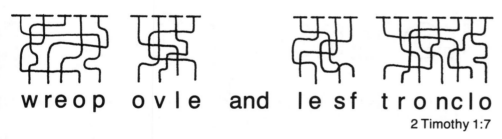

wreop   ovle   and   lesf   tronclo

2 Timothy 1:7

Who was holding the cloaks? Find his name by putting the first letter of each picture in the empty box

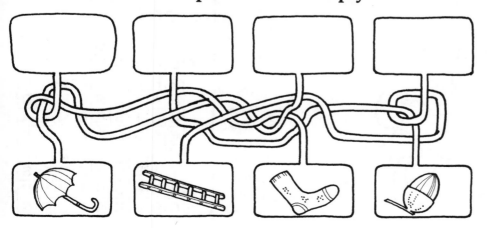

Word search

ANGER	HOLY SPIRIT
CITY	JESUS
CLOAKS	KNELT
CRY	SAUL
GLORY	STEPHEN
HEAVEN	STONING

C	R	R	E	G	N	A	E
R	L	H	L	N	C	G	I
C	A	O	T	Y	L	S	T
S	R	L	O	U	O	U	S
Y	N	Y	A	K	A	S	Y
J	E	S	U	S	K	H	P
S	H	P	J	E	S	E	I
A	P	I	G	T	N	A	R
U	E	R	P	L	I	V	I
Y	T	I	C	E	G	E	T
H	S	T	O	N	I	N	G
E	A	V	N	K	E	L	T

St Paul's Cathedral, London

Read the story in Acts 9

- Golden Gallery
- Stone Gallery
- Whispering Gallery

REMEMBER
- God hears our innermost thoughts
- A single ladder leads to the cross

Some facts about the Cathedral
- Old St. Pauls destroyed by fire in 1666
- Present Cathedral is about 300 years old
- It was designed by Christopher Wren
- The top of the cross is 111 metres high
- Charles and Diana married here in 1981

Jesus said: 'No one comes to the Father except through me'

(John 14:6)

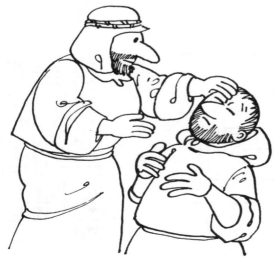

Word search

ANANIAS
BAPTISED
BLIND
CATHEDRAL
CROSS
DAMASCUS
DOME
GALLERY
LADDER
PAUL
WHISPERING

P	A	B	U	G	A	L	E	R
L	C	A	D	N	I	L	B	E
A	R	P	G	I	N	B	G	D
R	A	T	S	R	C	U	A	D
D	N	I	S	E	O	M	L	A
E	A	S	O	P	A	U	L	L
H	N	E	R	S	H	D	E	G
T	I	D	C	I	R	O	R	S
A	A	U	L	H	S	M	Y	U
C	S	P	B	W	T	E	O	G

1 Peter asleep

2 Friends pray

3 Peter awoken

4 Gates open

5 Peter knocks

6 Friends happy

The prayer of a good person has a powerful effect (James 5:16)

Help Peter find his friends

Read the story in Acts 16

Be joyful always, pray continually, give thanks in all circumstances for this is God's will for you in Christ Jesus (1 Thessalonians 5:16-17)

Word search

S	T	L	A	V	E	S	I	N	F	O	T
E	B	E	I	E	T	S	K	C	O	T	S
V	E	S	J	A	I	L	E	R	R	R	E	W
E	G	M	I	D	N	I	G	H	T	S	O	R
I	R	L	M	E	P	G	J	A	U	H	R
L	I	L	T	S	E	H	R	U	N	M	D
E	K	A	U	Q	H	T	R	A	E	H	T
B	E	S	T	A	S	S	G	N	T	D	S
B	P	N	S	I	P	A	O	S	E	I	P
G	N	I	G	N	I	S	W	R	L	D	E
E	V	A	L	S	I	R	P	A	L	O	C
O	M	H	P	R	E	T	S	N	E	L	G
S	K	C	P	O	C	K	S	L	R	I	G

BEATEN
BELIEVE
CHAINS
EARTHQUAKE
FORTUNE TELLER
GIRL
JAILER
LIGHTS
MAGISTRATES
MIDNIGHT
PAUL
PRISON
SILAS
SINGING
SLAVE
STOCKS
SWORD

Shade in every part that contains a dot

Paul shipwrecked

Acts 27

God will keep us safe!

SHIPWRECKED

How many words can you make using the letters in this word?

There are at least 30.

Word search

BOARD
BOAT
CARGO
GALE
LAND
PAUL
PRAY
ROME
SAFE
SAIL
SEA
SHIPWRECKED
SHORE
STORM

B	R	K	E	R	O	H	S	F	M	X	E
M	O	P	O	D	G	V	E	H	K	L	P
H	M	G	C	R	D	R	A	O	B	H	B
A	E	G	R	F	E	G	I	Z	O	U	A
Y	E	E	R	A	K	J	K	W	A	A	C
Z	C	L	M	A	C	N	E	U	T	V	E
D	O	P	D	R	E	Q	E	L	G	C	G
F	D	Z	A	Y	R	X	U	X	A	W	I
S	T	N	U	V	W	A	S	T	H	G	K
A	B	E	A	G	P	H	I	Z	K	E	M
F	O	Q	R	L	I	A	S	Y	M	X	O
E	L	Z	P	K	H	J	U	T	O	F	Q
M	M	R	O	T	S	V	A	S	Q	Y	S
X	C	D	F	M	B	W	Y	A	R	P	T

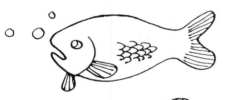

Which fish is different?

Put on the full armour of God

(Ephesians 6:11)

Word search

ARMOUR	PRAYER
ARROWS	SALVATION
BELT	SHIELD
BREASTPLATE	SHOES
FAITH	SWORD
HELMET	TRUTH

A	R	U	O	M	R	A	D	L
V	A	N	T	E	M	L	E	H
W	E	L	Y	T	H	O	T	S
S	A	A	V	I	R	R	A	H
L	R	E	O	D	U	L	L	I
P	R	S	R	T	V	L	P	E
A	O	O	H	A	W	H	T	L
O	W	E	T	H	B	S	S	D
S	S	I	N	T	S	H	A	B
R	O	H	F	I	L	O	E	U
N	M	S	E	A	O	E	R	M
A	R	R	O	F	N	S	B	I

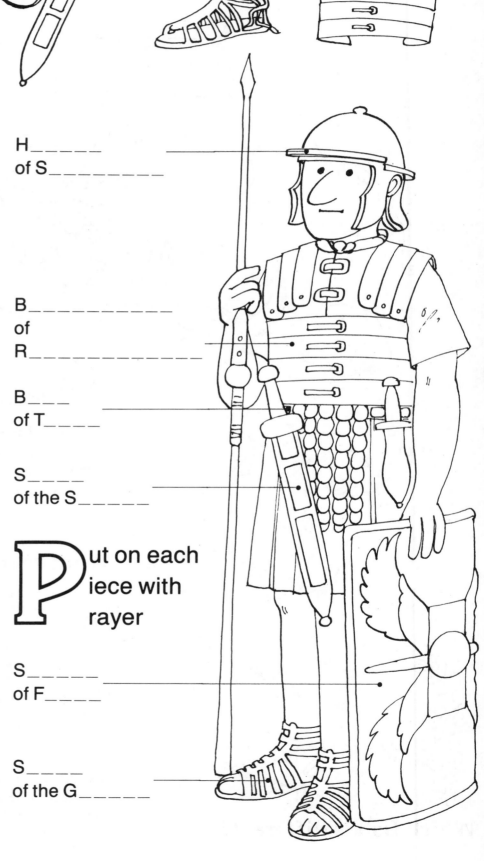

H_____
of S_____

B_____
of
R_____

B____
of T_____

S_____
of the S_____

Put on each **P**iece with **P**rayer

S_____
of F_____

S_____
of the G_____